It's a New Life!

Mom Is Gone

Steven B Salmon
Foreword by Larry Watson

Robert D. Reed Publishers

Robert D. Reed Publishers . Bandon, OR

Steven B. Salmon

Copyright © 2017 by Steven B. Salmon

All Rights Reserved.

Robert D. Reed Publishers
P.O. Box 1992
Bandon, OR 97411
Phone: 541-347-9882; Fax: -9883
E-mail: 4bobreed@msn.com
Website: www.rdrpublishers.com

Editors: Kristine Hanson and Cleone Reed
Cover Designer: Cleone Reed
Cover Photo by Dulce Fuentes
Painting of Author by Stasia Wilson
eBook Designer: Susan Leonard
Paperback formatter: Cleone Reed

Soft Cover ISBN: 978-1-944297-15-2
eBook ISBN 13: 978-1-944297-12-1

Library of Congress Control Number: 2016916925

Designed and Formatted in the United States of America

DEDICATION

The book is dedicated to Mary M. Salmon,
who dedicated and sacrificed her life
for me to become an author.

The book is dedicated to my four college classmates,
who always believe in me.
Thank you, Amber Tilley, David Strong,
Christine Evans, and Jessie Bushman.
This is our book.

The book is also dedicated to my cat, Lindy,
who sat behind me as I wrote day and night
writing the book in seven months.

Steven B. Salmon

ACKNOWLEDGMENTS

I want to personally thank my editor, Kristine Hansen, for editing the book and inspiring me. A thank you goes to my friend, Lisa Kaiser, an author, who I can share the highs and the lows of writing. Tina Schwartz, my agent, deserves credit for being the first professional person who believes in me. I have to thank my publisher, Cleone Reed, for publishing the book. Larry Watson, my mentor has inspired me throughout my life. Thanks Larry for giving me the strength to write after Mom passed away. I want to thank my family Susan Bain, Lexe and Courtney Bain, John DiVall, Jennifer Tonn, and Eric Johnson. Integrity Residential Services needs a huge thank you, especially Tim Hinze, my case manager Becky Bucda, and Gloreen Heft. The staff deserves a thank-you for putting up with an author. It's not easy to care for an author sometimes with my crazy hours and my mood swings. I have to thank Mike Lussenden, Bill Colby, Bob Curry, William Patrick Barlow, and Patti Huber. Patti was there for me with numerous emails of advice and encouragement. The following people need to be thanked: Stasia Wilson, Laurie Scheer, Christine DeSmet, Rita Angelni, Beth Engelhert, my brother Daro Saro, Leisure Flemming, Carey Hughes, Danny Riddle, Allen Bain, John Hinze, Mark Bain, Jon Bain, Josh Tilley, Tim Evans, Nancy Johns, Bobbi Johnson, Roxy Dennis, John Hinze, Jimmema Clark, Joyce DiVall, and Sara DiVall. I have to thank Visions Nightclub, especially Dave, Tabetha, and of course Nicki. There is one more person to thank, but I need to meet her yet.

TABLE OF CONTENTS

Painting of Steven B. Salmon by Stasia Wilson

ABOUT THE AUTHOR

Steven B. Salmon has severe cerebral palsy and uses a wheelchair which he drives with his head since he has little control of his hands. He writes using Morse code with his head. By tapping one letter at a time, he educates and shows the world that people with severe disabilities can contribute to society if given a chance to succeed. Much of his life he had been told by the system that he wasn't good enough to do anything. His mother dedicated and sacrificed her life for him to become an author and was his caregiver until her death, the event that precipitated this memoir.

His family, his friends (especially his four college class-mates), and his literary agent have always believed and supported his dreams, and his writing serves to give a voice for many who often do not have a voice.

Steven has a Bachelor of Science degree in English with a writing minor from the University of Wisconsin–Stevens Point where he graduated with honors. He earned an associate degree in Liberal Arts from Madison College where he freelances part-time as a writing assistant. Currently, he is writing his eighth novel. He lives with his cat Lindy in Madison, WI. He loves the outdoors, basketball, and the Green Bay Packers and enjoys being with people. As attested by his diligence, determination, and dedication, his main love in life is writing. As he says on his website,

www.stevensalmon.com,

"Not being able to speak is not the same
as not having anything to say."
~ Steven B. Salmon

Steven B. Salmon

FOREWORD

Writers often complain about how hard writing can be. Listening to them, you'd think that hanging sheetrock or tarring city streets in ninety-degree heat is nothing compared to the tortuous difficulty of typing words on a keyboard. Or—heaven forbid! —deleting those words or moving one of those unwieldy blocks of words to a new location. Maybe these complaining writers are secretly embarrassed about how easy they have it, and they cover their embarrassment by making the writing life sound as arduous as the bricklayer's. Or maybe they're just trying to discourage others from taking up the practice. After all, who needs more competition?

Yet there are writers for whom the movement of words from the brain to the page *is* a real travail. Steve Salmon is one of those writers. I've taught writing in colleges and universities for close to forty years, and I've seen many talented, skilled writers give up because the practice of the art was simply too difficult. Not one of them had to face on a daily basis the challenges that Steve faces writing sentences and paragraphs. Look at his website—stevenbsalmon.com—for a description of the process. You'll be amazed and humbled. (In brief, Steve doesn't have use of his hands, and he composes using Morse code, tapping out letters and words by moving his head, movement that is much harder for him than it is for most of us.)

But of course, there is a way that a writer's work can be harder than a ditch digger's, and it has to do with the part of the process that precedes finding the right words and putting them in the right order.

That work involves the excavation of the self, the willingness to dig deep into that part of ourselves where we try to keep our desires hidden and our fears buried. The unexamined life may not be, as Socrates said, worth living; but he didn't say the examination would be easy or painless. As it happens, I don't agree with Socrates' statement, mostly because writers often do the work for us; and when they dig deep enough, as Steve does in his honest, poignant memoir, they discover truths about themselves and about all of us. In the pages of *It's a New Life,*

Steven B. Salmon

Steve Salmon writes movingly about the loss of a parent, about the humiliations of ordinary life, about the frustrations of having ambitions that may not be realized, about desires that go unfulfilled, and about simple, unexpected joys. Steve's story is, in other words, our human story.

~ Larry Watson
Author of several novels, poetry, and short stories
English Professor, University of Wisconsin–Stevens Point for 25 years
See https://en.wikipedia.org/wiki/Larry_Watson_(writer)
And http://www.larry-watson.com/bio.htm

A SPECIAL NOTE
FROM THE PUBLISHER

When Steven's book was submitted to our publishing company, I found myself captivated and read and edited the entire book before I even responded to him. I wholeheartedly fell in love with his raw style of writing and his soulful authenticity.

One of my husband's and my favorite comedians of all time is a man named Josh Blue who won "Last Comic Standing" ten years ago (August 2006); and to this day, I often tell two of his jokes, always getting a laugh. Josh Blue also has cerebral palsy but much less severe that Steven's. Projecting my love for Josh on to Steven, I cracked up laughing at Steven's writing. Then I took a step back with the realization that this author is NOT Josh Blue but is Steven Salmon; and I started reading and editing with my heart rather than my funny bone, even though I still could imagine Josh borrowing material from Steven and in his own way making it funny. (See http://www.joshblue.com/.)

But there really isn't much if anything funny about Steven's life. Imagine being in a wheelchair, not able to do any of your own self-care, having minimal speech, yet, as he says, *"Just because I can't speak doesn't mean I don't have anything to say."* How many of us with all our capabilities have the diligence, determination, and dedication as Steven does to reach our full potential and dream big?

Steven Salmon has severe cerebral palsy and impressively holds a Bachelor's Degree in Writing from the University of Wisconsin–Stevens Point and spends some time every day at his craft—writing. Think of the comparison: I type 60 words a minute while Steven uses a form of Morse code and types one letter every two to four seconds. That translates to about four or five words a minute.

This memoir, *It's a New Life: Mom Is Gone*, gives the reader a real in-depth look (not just a peak) at what it is like to live with cerebral palsy, especially when thrust into independence in his 40's after his mother dies. Steven's writing is as raw, personal, and genuine as it gets. It automatically invites the reader to be

Steven's most avid cheerleader in life and gives us an inspirational kick in the butt to dream big too!

Sometimes people succeed in life because of who they know. Steven and I don't know anyone in common, to my knowledge; but there is something besides his writing, his personality, and the photos on his website that added to my desire to publish his work. He lives in Madison, Wisconsin, my home town. My family lives in Wisconsin. Steven and I both live on the very same Latitude Parallel north of the equator—43.1 degrees—only we are 1,755 miles apart as the crow flies!! My husband I met him a couple of weeks before his official launch of this book as an e-book on Amazon Kindle on his birthday, January 12, 2017! Almost two hours together, my admiration of him was confirmed.

~ Cleone Reed, Editor, Cover Designer, Publisher
Robert D. Reed Publishers, Bandon, OR

Cleone Reed meets Steven Salmon, December 27, 2016

Chapter One

FANTASY LAND

My new life is stressful at times. I have to be kind to my eight attendants who argue over small things like someone forgot to put the bed sheet on my bed or what happened to my washcloths. Then my mentally ill roommate will yell for no reason. My agent, Stasia, will email me to say that the manuscript needs more edits. It's time to go to the strip club to relax.

I wait for the bus to come to take me to the gentlemen's establishment. When the bus arrives, my attendant, James, opens the door to the garage. In an instant, I'm out of the garage. After being on the bus, the bus driver clamps down my electric wheelchair and takes the three yellow tickets from my backpack. I turn off the electric wheelchair's power switch button with my left balled fist. My hands are useless except my left can help me operate the electric wheelchair. I'm off for a night of fun.

In five minutes, I'm there! The bus driver unloads me in front of the strip club and helps me negotiate the narrow double doors. The second that I enter the entryway the scent of perfume hits me. It's a little after six so I don't have to pay to get in. It is VIP's hours. I park the electric wheelchair near the bar to watch the Brewers baseball, Packers football, or Bucks basketball on the big screen TV. The bartender cracks jokes with the regulars as he fills their orders. "The Packers defense sucks! We have no shot in the play-offs this year." The bartender's comment makes me laugh.

A beautiful brunette walks by me wearing a Milwaukee Bucks shirt. "Hi, handsome. Welcome back."

"Hi, Roxy." I watch her sit down at the bar.

"Hey there, Babe. How's it going?" A tall redhead asks me as she struts by in high heels and a pink negligee.

"Okay, Heather." I smile at her.

Another brunette walks by me in a halter top and a G-string saying, "Hi, Steven. How are you?"

"Okay, Chris." I'm smiling as I watch her go to the other side of the bar. I feel on the top of the world. All of my troubles just melt. The female attention is something of which I can't get enough. It makes me feel like a man, but I want to sit down and talk to them like my best friend, Amanda. I'm so lonely, but at that moment I'm a ladies' man! I sit there while listening to songs such as "*It's a New Life*" and "*Hey, Big Spender, Why Don't You Spend Some Time with me.*" I'm deciding who I will ask for a dance. I just want to relax for a while forgetting everything.

I'm a man with problems and a career like the men at the bar, as I try to find my place in the world. It's time to choose the woman that I want for a dance. My choice is Chris. I go over to her and say, "Hi, I want a dance."

"Do you have a twenty?"

"Yes," I say; I use my eyes to point to an envelope taped to my knee.

She removes the tape and opens it. After seeing the twenty-dollar bill, she tells me, "Follow me, Babe."

I follow her as she clears tables and chairs out of my way. My muscles are very tight. I'm excited.

"Nice and slow, Babe." She pulls a chair stuck in my front right wheel. Chris then gives my money to a man at a desk in the back. "Nick, I need a booth."

I wait for her to take out the chair and I carefully drive into my booth as she holds open the swinging doors for me.

When we are inside, she says, "Now don't run over my feet. Situate yourself."

After maneuvering the electric wheelchair in place, I turn it off.

The song, "*This Can't Be Happening*," plays as a stripper begins to dance on the runway. Chris has taken off her clothes. "You just relax and enjoy." She puts her leg on me to rub her vagina with her index finger. Chris flings her natural moisture at me. She places her breasts in my face. Chris turns around to rub her buttock against my boney knees for a minute. She sits in front of me to trace her finger around my mouth.

I'm in ecstasy for that moment. I just stare at her. It makes me wish that I can hold her in my lap, but my tight hamstrings make my knees go up making it impossible for her to sit on me. But the time ends with her. It leaves me empty inside and wanting more as she helps me get out of the booth.

"Thank you, Chris."

"Thank you, Steven." She goes to the bar and I go watch the strippers.

The rest of the evening I watch the ladies dance. I soak in the atmosphere with people talking and music playing. Sometimes men give me money to give to the women. They put the cash in my mouth. Then the stripper snatches the dollar from my mouth with hers. At times a stripper will put her breasts in my face, but the ladies have figured out that I have used my money and lose attention in me.

I have realized that it is a business, but it doesn't stop me from going to the strip club. One evening a man throws a wad of dollar bills in the air at a stripper. It rained money for a second.

About ten my bus picks me up to take me home. I have a big smile and I'm ready to handle my stressful life once again.

After the bus driver drops me off, I return to a quiet house. My roommates are in bed asleep. I will go to bed early. After I'm cleaned up, I will ask to be alone to masturbate. I imagine having sex with Chris as I rub my balled fist on my penis. When I'm about to come, I look to see the semen bursts from my cock. My imagination and the physical sensation allow me to picture what it is like to have intercourse with a woman.

Steven B. Salmon

Chapter Two

MOM, YOU NEED A DOCTOR

It is a typical day in first week of May, a Thursday, as my care attendant Ken raises me in the hoyer lift into my electric wheelchair. Ken and I are going to the Memorial Union to get out of the condominium for a few hours to escape the isolation. When Ken positions me in my electric wheelchair, we hear a faint call for "help."

"I'll be right back." Ken leaves my room to see what is wrong with Mom.

I'm thinking about what I need to write when I come home. I let out a big yawn.

Several minutes later, Ken returns to my bedroom and says, "Your Mom has fallen. I have picked her up and put her in the recliner in the living room."

I don't think much of it. My mind is elsewhere looking forward to being out.

Ken takes me to the bathroom, puts on my shoes, brushes my teeth, and we go out to the dining room to eat.

He begins to feed me lunch when Mom starts to stand up and falls again. Ken rushes over to her and helps Mom to her bed.

Now I know how serious it is. I wait until Ken comes back and says, "We'll forget going.   I'll cancel the bus." He goes into the kitchen to call the bus. Ken feeds me the rest of my lunch.

I'm worried about Mom, but I don't know what to do. My case manager, Becky, rings the intercom. It's time to do the annual income review to determine if my income doesn't exceed a certain limit to remain eligible to receive home health care.

Ken answers the door.

We sign the paperwork while the three of us talk about Mom.

"I'll go talk to Mary." Becky disappears into Mom's bedroom.

I eavesdrop and hear Becky tell Mom, "You need to see a doctor. Please call 911."

"No, I'm okay. Thank you. I just need to rest."

I ask Becky when she comes back, "What do I do now?"

"Start emailing for help, Steven. I'll be at the office until five. Email me if you need help."

Ken transfers me from the electric wheelchair to the manual wheelchair. Then he sets me up at my desk. Ken turns on the computer and puts on the head array on the back of the manual wheelchair. "I'll be back around four to feed you supper." He pushes his bicycle out the door.

"Okay." I start tapping away an email to my sister to get help. After I activate Mouse Mode to move the mouse, I double-click my word prediction program called CoWriter and then open Outlook Express. I move the mouse up to click on the inbox to open my email. After I exit Mouse Mode, I use Control and H to hide the word prediction window. I do the code for Shift Tab to highlight the first email in the inbox. Then I tap Control and N to create a New Message. I spell the letters "ly" and my sister's email address pops in the To box. The slow process frustrates me but I have no choice as I Shift Tab twice to the Subject Line. The letters of "Help Mom" appears. I Shift Tab one more time to the text message box before I use the equals sign to bring up the CoWriter window. Then I begin to type the message that reads:

Lynn,
Mom has fallen several times today. She refuses to go to the doctor. Mom can't stand up. You need to come now!
Steven

I cc the email to my two cousins, Mac and Jill, before I tap Alt and S to send it. Then I write an email to my two college classmates. The message reads:

Mom has fallen several times today and won't go to the doctor. I emailed Lynn. I'm waiting for her reply.
Steven

I send it off. Then I hear a ding. I see the reply from my sister and I click on it. The message reads:

Who is Mom's doctor? What clinic does she go to? Should I come now or wait?

I reply.

Mom doesn't have a doctor or a clinic. COME NOW!

I send it and wait. A minute later, Lynn answers.

I'm coming. I'll be there in two hours. Please tell Mom that I'm coming.

I answer.

Okay.

Ken comes back now. He has a key to the condominium that Mom has given him. Ken checks on Mom first. He returns to the large living rooms and says, "I'll fix supper." Ken goes into the kitchen and cooks.
I email Lynn again.

I'll keep the porch door open for you. Steven

Lynn replies.

Okay, thanks. I'm on my way.

I notice food on the table.
Ken takes me off the computer and assists me with the bathroom. He has soup, garlic bread, and green beans ready.
It isn't Mom's good cooking, but it will do. I'm eating when Mom pushes herself in one of my old manual wheelchairs to the dining room table. I continue to eat as Mom eats. "Lynn is coming, Mom."
"There is no need for her to come. You have overreacted, Steven. When will she be here?"
"Soon." I finish supper. "Thank you. I want to write. Please leave the porch door open."
Ken says, "Okay. Let's set you back up. I have to get to my other client's." Ken brushes my lap with a towel and puts back

the computer. He cleans the dishes and pushes his bicycle out of the porch door. Ken leaves the door cracked open.

Mom has disappeared to her room.

I go back to emailing my friends when Mom reappears in the old manual wheelchair.

Mom maneuvers the old manual wheelchair to the porch window. She sits there as she waits for Lynn to come.

I'm in my writing zone. It's just me writing when I see Lynn at the door.

"What's going on, Mom?" Lynn steps inside the porch.

"I'm okay. I'll go to Urgent Care tomorrow."

"Well, I'm here now and you have no choice."

"I'll go in the morning."

I look at Mom and say in a firm voice, "You are going now, Mom."

That was the end of the discussion. Lynn gathers Mom's things and pushes her out of the front door. I return back to the computer.

"Get your care attendant to stay overnight. I'll keep you posted." Lynn closes the front door and leaves.

"Okay." I keep on tapping away. I email Ken to ask him to spend the night. The rest of the evening, I play email tag with Lynn. My mom's condition turns to worse. I sit in the spacious living room as I tap in silence. The emails from Lynn are discouraging. One of the last emails from Lynn reads:

> *Steven,*
> *Please get me your case manager's phone number. Mom won't be able to care for you anymore. Everything is normal but she can't stand up. Mom will be going to assisted living for a while.*

It hits that my life is going to change but I don't really comprehend it. I email to give Lynn my case manager's email address and say that I'm shutting down the computer.

Ken arrives a couple of minutes later. He puts me to bed. Ken sleeps on the sleeper sofa in the living room.

I don't remember much about the next day except emailing my friends. Mom was stable, but she was in a confused state. What I do remember is an email from my best friend, Amanda. The message reads:

Steven,
I'm very worried for your mom. Amanda

The email doesn't register in my mind. I'm in shock, but I believe that Mom will be back in a few days.

The next day is pretty much the same. I email my friends or reply to emails. My sister, Lynn, doesn't want me to be alone. She cleans the condominium instead of going to the hospital to see Mom.

I don't understand why Lynn doesn't leave me by myself since I'm always alone. But a fire can happen or some emergency like me falling out of my wheelchair.

Mom was always there. But at times it felt that I was all alone. I remembered not being able to wake up Mom at night to go to bed. There were nights I called for Mom for hours, but I just sat at the computer to write or email until Mom woke up. Writers kept me company those nights. I liked and wanted to be alone in order to write. And now someone had to be with me.

When Ken arrives at four, Lynn goes to the hospital to see Mom. He feeds me before he helps me to get back on the computer. Ken is my care attendant for the last two years. The open dining and living room is silent as we eat pizza. Coal, my black cat, is taking a bath in Mom's recliner while my gray cat, Ashes, lopes by me as I begin to write. The sun is beginning to set. When Ken goes, I see the maple tree is budding outside of the sun porch window.

I'm alone to write emails. I don't recall who I emailed. My network of friends keeps me busy.

My cousin, Jay, and his wife, Ming, appear at the porch screen door. The door is left open a crack to allow people to take the key to the condominium to open the front door, but the inside door to the porch is locked. Jay and Ming enter through the front door. He says, "How are you? Writing again?"

"Yeah, that's what I do." I'm mad at Lynn. I don't want Jay here.

"Well, we won't bother you." Jay sits on the sofa while Ming sweeps the floor.

I continue to write emails until ten. "Jay, I'm done. Please take me off computer."

"My pleasure, Steven." He gets up to remove the head array from the back of the manual wheelchair. Jay pushes me to the TV to watch the Dodgers and the Brewers.

Then Lynn and my cousin, Jill, come into the condominium. Lynn says, "Steven, we need to talk." She sits down in front of me. "Mom passed away."

I don't respond. It doesn't feel that Mom is gone. I'm numb. This has been in the back of my mind for years and its reality. My biggest fear has come true.

"Mom passed away, Steven. She went into cardiac arrest when I got there. They did everything that they could do. I'm sorry."

Jill pats my shoulder. "Mac is coming from Minneapolis. He'll be here soon."

I don't cry or say anything for several minutes. I'm dumbfounded. I want my college classmates. I'm breaking inside. My classmates are the best people, especially my friends, Amanda and Dan. "I want to write."

"Okay." Lynn puts back on the computer.

I open up my email and write a massive email to my friends. The subject line reads: Mom passed. The message says:

Mom passed away tonight. I need you now! Amanda and Dan, I need to see you. I'm ready to break. Please come now. You promised me. Steven

I sit there for several minutes until I hear two dings. The two replies are from my two best friends. The emails make me cry.

You got it. Dan

We'll be there in the morning. Amanda

Chapter Three

BEAVER RIVER
COMES TO THE RESCUE

I shut down the computer again. I sit at my desk thinking about Amanda and Dan coming to visit me when Ken pushes his bicycle through the porch doors.

"Hi, everyone. What's going on?" Ken takes off his bicycle helmet after he places the bike next to my electric wheelchair.

I look at Lynn and then at Ken. "Sit down, Ken." After I take a deep breath, I start to cry, but I manage to get the words out. "Mom passed away, Ken. I'm sorry."

"What?" Then Ken brawls like a baby and almost falls out of the chair.

"Help him! He's delicate!" I stare at Lynn and Jill. My sister and cousin rush to console Ken. I'm beyond numb. I feel lost, but I do hear Ken when he says, "Mary was my only friend. She always greeted me with a smile on my face. Mary was my Mom, too."

After Ken calms down, I tell him, "We'll work through this together."

"Okay."

"Now I need to go to bed because Beaver River is coming tomorrow." My two best friends teach at Northland High School in Beaver River. When I talk about Beaver River, I'm referring to Amanda and Dan. All that I ever talked about was Beaver River. It has always been my dream to go to Beaver River. When I email my best friends, I always address the email to "Beaver River" or "Beaver River teachers."

"Let's get you in bed then. I'm staying the night and I'll get you early," says Ken. He gives me my muscle-relaxation medication with a root beer, takes me to the bathroom, and puts me to bed.

I can't sleep. I'm heartbroken about Mom. It's hard to believe that she is gone. What will I do now? I hear Lynn, Jill, and

Ken talking in the living room. I cry softly to myself. My cat, Ashes, runs around the condominium after Jay and Ming leaves. Doors are being opened and closed. The once silent house is no more. I try to sleep, but instead I weep. The red digits on the clock radio slowly flash as morning approaches. Just when I'm about to fall asleep, I hear my cousin Mac enter the condominium.

"Is he awake? I have to talk him," Mac says to Lynn and Jill.

"Leave him be," Jill tells Mac.

He doesn't listen and knocks on my bedroom door. Mac enters my room.

I'm awake.

He sits down on my bed. "I'm sorry about your Mom. After forty-seven years, you are an adult now. Welcome to the real world, where shit flies"

I don't know what he is talking about as Coal jumps up on my bed to purr in my ear. Coal's tail is shaped into a question mark. He stares at me before he curls into a ball beside me.

"You'll have to start wearing Depends, you know."

"Yes, I know." I fall asleep for half an hour. Then I wake up to think about Beaver River.

I need my two best friends from college. Amanda and Dan always inspire me through the tough times. When I graduated from college, I tried to get hired as a writing tutor at the technical college. I wanted to work with people, but my speech had deteriorated. I tried to be an online writing assistant, but I needed an Education degree to work. The only answer was for me to go back to school. But my college classmates reminded me that I needed to write.

I spent endless hours writing manuscripts that I tried to market to publishers and agents only to get rejected. My classmates said, "Keep at it, Steven." When I did publish, my books didn't sell and the local news ignored me. My friends said, "Write another book."

For every step that I took it was two steps backwards. I emailed Amanda and Dan each week to tell them what I was doing. Sometimes I emailed my classmates numerous times in a week or even in a day. A typical email to Beaver River read:

Dear Beaver River,

It's a New Life! Mom is Gone

You got snow. Madison has about fifty inches already! In fact, it's snowing right now. I'm sick of snow! It better not snow the second weekend of April during the writing conference. I will be honored in front of four-hundred writers as a part of the conference's luncheon success panel. Imagine that! I'm just a writer. Stasia is reading my speech. I still can't believe that we have an agent. The middle-grade manuscript is about ready to send to her. I'm tired! I have been writing this book for ten hours each day for the last year. Someday we'll be a best-selling author. I know, I know, I'm dreaming. New York, that's our goal. Steven

I live a writer's life. When "my" agent offered to "coach" me, I spent countless hours to try to impress her by rewriting and editing a children's book multiple times. My classmates pushed me onwards to get Stasia to represent me. It was a continuous process of rewrites that made me mad at Stasia, but I took my frustrations out on my classmates who told me to cool it. A month later I had a contract with Stasia.

My classmates taught me to believe in myself, be patient, and never give up. When Stephen King's agent rejected my two books that I spent eight months rewriting, my friends emailed words of encouragement. They read thousands of emails about my fears, failures, successes, and my impatience. But my classmates were the first to witness my passion to write that lit up the night, but only a few saw.

My roommate's guardian asked my roommate. "Is that Steven, who writes books? He doesn't look like he could write." Amanda and Dan know the real Steven as do the rest of my friends. Nothing can stop me, but since Mom has passed all I want is Amanda and Dan.

I get up and wait for my friends to come. When the intercom buzzes at nine, Lynn goes to the outside door to bring Amanda and Dan inside of the condominium. I start to cry when I hear the series of doors open and close. My muscles are very tight. The second that I see my dear friends, I break down. Lynn and Jill leave us alone.

"You are here! You came!" Tears roll down my cheeks as Amanda and Dan walk into the condominium.

"How's the author?" Dan gives me a bear hug as Amanda pats my shoulder.

I collapse into their arms.

"Let it all out, Steven." Amanda wipes away my tears with a Kleenex.

After several minutes, I gather myself together and begin to talk as my two friends sit on the sofa. What would I do without you, Amanda, and my cats? You're my inspiration! Mom is gone. I love Mom. She read me like a book. She spoiled me. Cared for me all of my life! She never complained or wanted anything. But Mom's over-protective behavior in the last years made me hate Mom at times. Everything revolved the weather! Mom stayed at home except for going to the bank, post office, grocery store, Walgreens, and the farmers' market. All she talked about was the farmers' market. It drove me nuts! I gave up going out because of the weather. She made me miss a day of the writing conference due to a chance of a thunderstorm. Of course nothing happened! It's just another missed rare opportunity to get out of the house. When I took the bus, she stared out of the window to wait for the bus. Once when I was late, Mom called the bus. It embarrassed me. She wanted to know where I was going and who I was going with or who was meeting me. I couldn't make my own decisions. I tried to be independent. She forgot things. There were times that Mom didn't hear me. She shook the fork or the spoon when she fed me. When Mom took me to the doctor's office for an appointment, she became lost. Mom just drove around the neighborhood. But Mom wanted to be in charge. I took over managing my care and being an author. Care workers came and went like the wind. That was why I stayed here with Mom. Attendants were not like Mom! Mom was one of a kind. I'm spoiled!" Tears glide down my cheeks. I stare at my friends

"We've been through this, Steven. We know that you're scared. Remember our promise we made to you when we were in college about never leaving you, and making sure you are taken care of?" Dan replies.

"Yeah, but I haven't seen you for ten years. It's surreal that you're here."

"Well, we're here! We promised you that we would come. And I'll visit more, I promise you."

"You'll get busy and forget me," I tell them with tears in my eyes.

"You're stuck with us. We need you! And one of us will stay until we're confident that our author is all right on your own. You've a new book to market to publishers and have Stasia, your agent," Dan tells me.

"Yeah, but. I'm just a failure! Having an agent is just a lot of work. My family doesn't understand like you do," I say.

"Fuck them!" Dan exclaims.

My cousin, Mac, touched me on my arm saying, "I'm here for you." I nod and say, "I need them now." Mac goes into the messy kitchen with its dirty dishes, paperwork, unpaid bills, and old food. "Do you remember when snow fell on the first of May, and the university shut down during finals week?"

Amanda says, "Yes, I do! I had to pull your electric wheelchair out of a snow bank. You were not paying attention to where you were going. You're a reckless driver." I say, "I'm not. I never ran over women."

"That's a lie. When you saw a pretty girl, you ran into walls, doors, and trees." Amanda tells me. I laugh.

Then I ask. "Can I do this?"

My friends say. "Yes, you can!" Amanda chimes in. "And you will! I have high expectations of you and your future!"

"Absolutely! You've got to keep moving forward and writing," Dan tells me.

"I do have a career and an agent." I reply.

Amanda answers. "Remember, you've got a lot to live for."

I say with tears, "I will, I promise. New York someday," I say.

"Exactly," my friends reply in unison.

I start to close my eyes, but I want to be with Beaver River.

"It is okay, Steven. Go to sleep. We're here. Sleep Steven."

I fall asleep as they hold me.

Mac keeps pacing back and forth in the closet, chomping his fingernails. When he chews one nail down to the nub, Mac starts chewing on the next fingernail.

"Will you relax?" Lynn exclaims.

Amanda bumps Mac when she enters into the walk-in closet.

"Excuse me," Amanda says, before walking over to grab a pair of soiled blue jeans from a yellow plastic container.

"You don't have to do that, Amanda. I will," Lynn replies.

"Don't be silly. That's why we're here to help out," Amanda says

She disappears back into the kitchen with the dirty jeans to soak them in bleach. I hear her run the water at the kitchen's sink.

Chapter Four

THEN THERE IS MY COUSIN MAC

Mac begins to fidget. He stuffs his hands in his pockets. A second later, he yanks his hands out of the jeans. His arms swing from his sides as he increases his pacing. Mac stares at Lynn while biting the fingernails on his right hand.

"After all these years, he doesn't let anyone take him to the bathroom, or clean up his shit except for your Mom and Dad. Then he lets total strangers take care of him. And they all know about his dirty secret. You know, he'll have to wear Depends. Steven should have been in them years ago," Mac says.

Mom hand-washed my dirty jeans and briefs in the kitchen sink. She washed soiled washcloths in the kitchen. Mom did this unsanitary practice all of my life after I attended a two-week summer camp when I was eight, and the camp counselors made me wear diapers. Mom promised me that I didn't have wear diapers after I threw a temper tantrum. When I started to receive home health care, my care attendants and nurse suggested that I start wearing Depends. I was embarrassed, but I learned that some disabled people wore adult diapers. If I wanted to be independent, I would have to wear Depends. I started the process of moving out four months before Mom passed away. My case manager, Becky, was helping me to move to an apartment. In fact, I was getting to know a roommate at that time. I was prepared to wear diapers. Mac and Lynn were surprised that I agreed to wear Depends just two days after Mom's death. It was a new life. And I was ready to enter it.

"I know. But first off, they're not strangers! Amanda and Dan are Steven's best friends from college. Steven will listen to them," Lynn replies.

"I used to be his God growing up. I'm the only one who takes him places," Mac says.

"That's not true! All of us should have helped Mom more. We should have visited more often. She never asks, wants, or expects anything. Mom gave her life and heart for Steven. It shouldn't have happened! But..." Lynn says, stopping mid-sentence.

"I know! I know!" Mac starts to pace again.

Mac has always had a big heart. He's taken me to sporting stadiums like Lambeau Field, County Stadium, Bradley Center, Metrodome, and Wrigley Field. When wheelchair's tickets to Packers game were unavailable at Lambeau Field, Mac managed to find wheelchair's tickets for the Packers Chiefs game at Arrowhead Stadium in Kansas City. He called Mom to see if I wanted to go. After Mom agreed to the football adventure, he ordered the tickets and reserved hotel rooms.

Mom drove from Stevens Point, where I attended college, to Minneapolis where Mac worked as a news cameraman. Mac then drove us from Minneapolis to Kansas City while she slept in the back. He needed her to take me to the bathroom. Mac tried to get her to go shopping or go to the game, but she refused, staying behind at the hotel and watching television. After the game, he took me back to the hotel to urinate before we returned to Minneapolis.

It was my first Packers game, and the first time I saw Brett Favre play live on the field. The Packers lost by ten points. Even so Mac and I wore enormous smiles on our faces all the way back Minneapolis.

When I traveled anywhere, Mom had to tag along to help me to use the urinal. She would always meet Mac or my brother-in-law, Mark, in Appleton in order for me to attend Packers games in Green Bay. Mom walked around the mall, waiting for the game to be over. She smoked in the parking lot as she waited for me to return from the game. Then she helped me use the urinal before our drive home.

I allowed Mac to help me with the urinal once when we attended the NCAA Basketball Tournament in Milwaukee. I was twenty-five years old. After the first session of the first round of the tournament, Mac and I went back to the van in the parking garage. Once I was inside of the van, I said, "I got to go."

Mac didn't know how to respond at first, but both of us knew I needed to urinate at some point during the long day. He retrieved the urinal from my backpack. Mac then unzipped my fly and pulled down my underwear. Mac aimed and held my penis for me to urinate.

I went pee. It was three ounces, which was normal for me. I laughed and gagged. It pleased me that I had success in urinating.

Mac made a joke out of it while he put me back together. He snickered, "You stubborn asshole! You just did a piddle. You didn't really have to go! You should have done it inside the Bradley Center. Now we've got to carry your whiz around with us until we find a toilet to dump it. Thanks a lot!" Mac said.

I didn't like using public restrooms. The disinfectant smell made me gag. I needed absolute privacy in order to pee. For instance, I used to hold my urine all day at school until I returned home.

When I visited my grandparents in Lancaster, Wisconsin, I held my urine from Springfield, Ohio, all the way to Davenport, Iowa. This is a twelve-hour drive. Davenport had a rest stop without a public restroom. I allowed my father, Patrick, to carry me past a brown picnic shelter with an orange hand pump for well water to a stand of pine trees.

Dad would stand behind me, holding me upright before unzipping my jeans. I looked at the used strands of toilet paper lying in the tall grass, making me want to gag. I watched a cow urinate in a muddy pasture. The hissing sound helped me go pee. I urinated while smelling fresh cow dung and watching cows chew away at a round bale of hay. Staring at the run-down farm in the distance and being outdoors made it easier for me to go pee.

"I won't ever understand why you can't just go like everyone else." remarked Mac, putting the semi-filled urinal back in the backpack.

I laughed and drooled, choosing to ignore Mac's question.

For years, Mac told the story about me to his colleagues and friends about the time when I made him take me to the bathroom in the van.

"Hey, have I ever told you about the time when Numbnuts piddles in the parking garage, and makes me tote his whiz around downtown Milwaukee?" Mac would ask, before launching into his story.

It embarrassed me, but Mac liked to be loud.

Mac cared deeply about me. He managed to convince his news producer to let him shoot digital tape of me when my first book was released. Mac didn't like how the local newspapers and television stations ignored the press releases I sent out, suggesting a story about a Cerebral palsy author. How many severely physically disabled people wrote novels like me? He knew I needed more opportunities, and Mom needed help caring for me. Mac traveled from Minneapolis down to a small Wisconsin town called Poynette to shoot the video.

Mom moved to Poynette after I earned my Bachelor of Science in English from Stevens Point. She found a wheelchair accessible condominium with a roll-in-shower.

Mac shot the video of me, reading at the dining room's table, showing how I sat at the computer all afternoon, spelling out every letter of each word that I wrote. He shot a segment of Ashes, jumping up onto the kitchen counter, begging for food while Mom fixed our supper. Mac asked my mom, "What are your hopes for Steven for the future?"

She rocked back and forth in her recliner before saying, "Steven needs to be around people who take the time to see the many talents that he has to offer. He needs more to do and places to go. That's my wish for Steven."

I only left the condominium between forty-five and fifty days out of the year. That was only six or seven weeks out of an entire year. I could always remember the exact day I had last left the house, and where I went. The doctor's office, the barber shop, Barnes & Noble, Target, and the technical college were the only places that I frequented. It wasn't unusual for several weeks to go by with me not seeing another person (outside of my mother) or going anywhere. When I lived in Poynette, I critiqued papers for a couple of my former instructors from the technical college. Mom would take me to Madison several times a semester to pick up and return papers. It was a part-time job for a few times a year, but it allowed me to get out of the house. Time seemed to slip with each day I spent sitting at the computer writing about the past.

Mac began to notice changes in my attitude after I graduated from college. He called Mom one evening to ask if I wanted to see LeBron James play the Bucks in Milwaukee.

"No," I answered.

It puzzled Mac that I didn't want to go because he knew I was a LeBron James fan and never missed a Bucks game. He called again to see if I wanted to catch the Los Angeles Dodgers play the Brewers at Miller Park.

"No," I said.

Mac couldn't believe I didn't want to go out with him anymore. In the past, each time Mac offered to take me to a game I jumped at the chance. When Mac visited, he tried to get me out of the house to go to a movie or to a bar.

"No," I said.

Once when Mac visited us in Poynette, Mac paced back and forth in the living room, shuffling his hands. He picked at his nails.

Saliva dripped from my red fat lower lip onto the laminated hard wood floor. I sat in my manual wheelchair as we watched the Lakers and the Warriors.

Mac walked behind me while he jabbed his fingers into my neck and shoulders. Then he rubbed my right ear with his left index finger.

How come you don't want to go out?" Mac asked. "Let's go somewhere! I'm bored! Let's go to a bar and get drunk!"

I laughed. It was about midnight. I had taken my last dose of Baclofen, a medication to relax my tense muscles. I didn't know that I could have alcohol with Baclofen, but Mom believed the rehabilitation doctor who said I shouldn't. Alcohol made me sleepy, and I wanted to be awake when Mac visited or when we went somewhere.

A minute later, I let out a big yawn.

"What are you tired for? You don't work! All you do is read, write, critique writing, eat, shit in your pants, watch sports, and sleep until ten. You're a lazy son of bitch!" Mac replied.

"Fuck you! I have a new book ready. Writing is working!" I said.

Mac laughed saying, "Come on now, all you write about is you, and your problems that no one cares about! You should write television shows like Desperate Housewives and The Bachelor. Now *that's* great writing! Not that disabled self-pity crap like being unemployable, and not being able to live where you want that you waste your time writing about."

I glared at Mac. My arms flew about. I spat drops of drool in the air by accident. "Go to hell! One day I will be known!" I said.

Mac laughed, wiping the saliva from his face with a Kleenex.

"Gross! You really sprayed me good that time! Who says that you'll be a known author?" Mac asked, laughing as we watched the Lakers Warriors game. "What you need is culture in your life!"

What Mac meant by culture was reading newspapers, watching ESPN News all day to stay current with the sporting news, and traveling places. It upset Mac when I didn't know the batting averages of the Milwaukee Brewers versus the Chicago Cubs or the daily NFL injured report. He read newspapers, *Sports Illustrated*, and news-oriented websites. Mac traveled to New York, Philadelphia, Boston, England, Oregon, California, and Alaska on the spur of the moment.

I emailed queries and received rejections from around the United States, the United Kingdom, and the Soviet Union. Sometimes I emailed my publisher in Baltimore. I had dreams of going to New York and appearing on the Today Show to talk about my most recent book. My writing career had given me the privilege of meeting literary agents, authors, editors, publishers, and writers at writing conferences. Being a Forensics teaching assistant at the technical college allowed me to see the technical college's theater productions for free.

"My friends Amanda and Dan, they believe!" I said.

"What do they know?" Mac replied, staring at me. "All you talk about is Amanda and Dan. You barely email me anymore."

"I'm busy! I email Amanda and Dan. We're working on a book to teach to students. They're helping me write it. They understand. That's our dream! Without them I give up! I miss them!" I said as I cried.

It scared Mac to see how isolated and delicate I had become in my early thirties. Mac drove down the interstate past the lighted skyscrapers of Minneapolis towards the Excel Center where he and I had tickets to see the Minnesota Wild play the Saint Louis Blues. The car radio blasted Megadeath while Mac pretended to play an air guitar in his lap.

I laughed at my hyperactive cousin, passing traffic in the fast lane, barreling towards downtown. Staring at the lights of the tall glass office buildings, I was trying to enjoy the moment, but I knew that when the weekend was through it was back to being isolated.

Mac slapped my boney right knee, making my entire body very tight.

"Chill out! Boy, you're jumpy these days! I'm going to make you love hockey! It's the best sport in the world!" Mac told me.

During most of the game I stared at my right palm, drooling into my open hand, watching spittle cascade along my thin long life line. "We'll Rock You" and "Welcome to the Jungle" blared away.

Mac engrossed himself in the game. He pranced in front of his seat, yelling and studying each player's move.

Suddenly the crowd erupted. A towering blue light glared.

A loud fog horn blew causing me to almost jump out of my manual wheelchair. My balled fist accidentally hit Mac in the crotch.

He grabbed his balls. "You got me good that time!" Mac said.

I laughed, staring at the flashing towering blue light in the right corner of the arena that looked like a lighthouse.

"Did you see that fricking power play that the Wild scored?" Mac shouted.

Mac rubbed his right index finger on my left ear. When Mac became anxious, he rubbed my ear. For some unknown reason when Mac saw me staring at the blue light, he yelled, "I take you to your first hockey game. There's a power play, and you miss it! All you do is sit staring at your hands and the stupid light!"

I didn't like hockey, having a memory of a Detroit Red Wings goalie, coughing up blood on the ice after being hit with a pluck on Sports Center. It made me sick to my stomach I had traveled to Minneapolis to be on TV, not to see a hockey game.

Mac stood jabbering about the game in the hotel room, watching ESPN. He paced back and fourth eating potato chips. Mac yawned.

"Well, I better get back to the station to edit the author's videotape for the morning news. I can't believe that he doesn't like hockey! It's awesome, but he will not give it a try. Well, I should go now to dub the tape. I guess."

"Go," I replied.

"I should be going," he said as he started to stand up. But Mac sat back down again when The Top Ten Plays aired. "I have to check out The Top Ten Plays first, and then I'll go."

"Go Gravel! Go!"

In the seventh grade, Mac and I attended the same junior high school after my parents moved from Springfield, Ohio to Lancaster, Wisconsin. I noticed that all of Mac's classmates called him by his last name of Gravel. The name stuck since I didn't have trouble saying Gravel. I remember being at a high school football game with Mac and my father. By the middle of the fourth quarter the game was decided. My father wanted to go home, but Mac had disappeared with his friends. I screamed "Gravel" several times.

He appeared. "Yeah, what do you want?" Mac asked.

"Go home." I motioned my eyes at Dad who then saw Mac, and Dad pointed to the exit.

"I'll go when I feel like it," he laughed at me. He stood up and then he made his way to the door, heading to the parking lot. "All right, I get the picture. But I want to know, am I your God?" Mac asked me.

"You know, it's you!"

Mac snickered before opening the hotel door.

My entire body jerked when the door clicked shut. The phone rang around eight o'clock; waking me up made my muscles spasm. When I heard a loud noise, my muscles automatically jerked making my stiff body jump from my startle reflex that I developed as a baby.

Mom answered the phone.

"Hello, Mac. Yes, he's awake! At 8:14 Steven's story will be on your station. Channel fifteen."

She turned on the television and switched to Mac's news station.

"I got it! Oh, we'll have a good day. He's grinning from ear to ear. We'll see you, tonight. Thanks, Mac."

She hung up the receiver and sat on the bed. She and I watched the video that Mac shot at Poynette with me reading a book at the dining room table while Mom turned pages for me. The next part showed me spelling out words on the computer. One by one letters slowly popped up on the computer screen. The next piece had Ashes scurrying across the kitchen counter and me saying, "Get down, Ashes."

Then Mac interviewed Mom and a couple of my writing professors from Stevens Point. Professor Barlow said, "Steven wanted to be treated like a regular college student, and he didn't want any special favors. His work was meticulous and done on time."

Larry Watson, the acclaimed novelist, who taught Writing courses at Stevens Point and wrote the books *Justice* and *Montana 1948* said, "Steven has found his writing voice. There's no telling how far he can go."

The black anchorwoman, Leisure Roads, held my book in front of the camera saying, "Steven's book is available on Amazon.com. He writes to improve the lives of the physically disabled. He's an inspiration."

I laughed.

Either people believed I'm an inspiration or a severely retarded person. I treasured being "just Steven" to Amanda and Dan.

"Wait until I tell Amanda and Dan. I'm an inspiration!"

Mom began to undress my lower half. She put on my underwear and socks and then blue jeans on my tight boney legs. The phone rang. She answered it.

I yelled, "Thank you, Gravel! You're my God! Now maybe people will listen!"

"Yes, he's excited, Mac," Mom told him.

"I did it!"

I wished the local news media had responded to the press releases I'd emailed so I could be a hero in my own community.

Steven B. Salmon

Chapter Five

AN AUTHOR'S LIFE

An author's life meant living with the highs and the lows. It hurt me that my achievements often went unrecognized. At times I didn't have the capability of email, and I didn't know how to write a proper synopsis for one of my books. In the years to come, I gained the ability of email. I also attended writing conferences to improve my writing.

Each day I kept up my writing holding tight to the dream of being interviewed on the news. I wanted to show the news media my writing talent deserved to be known. When I saw an author being interviewed on the local television, I yelled at the screen, "One day, I'm coming with my agent. You will hear about it! Someday, my agent will be calling you! Dumb media! Someday, I will win!"

News directors wanted authors who did book signings at bookstores. Local bookstores didn't want to stock my book unless I had a literary agent. I met and pitched manuscripts to agents at writing conferences where I sat, staring and drooling at the panel of literary agents from Los Angeles and New York, who patiently answered other writers' questions at the Writers' Institute conference in Madison, Wisconsin. I waved my left balled fist. An agent called on me, "Sir, what's your question?" I always brought an interpreter along to writing conferences to ask questions on my behalf and verbally make my pitches to agents. My interpreter stood up with a sheet of paper in her hand. The person looked at me before directing my question to the panel. "Steven writes novels that feature characters with severe Cerebral palsy. He wants to know if he should give up writing about characters with severe Cerebral palsy in order to find an agent to represent him." All of the agents reassured me that I was writing what I needed to write, and applauded my efforts.

Inspired by this, I emailed manuscripts to agents, hoping to get a yes. Time kept passing as I moved forward in my writing, waiting to hear back from agents. To my disappointment, I received "nice" rejections.

Dear Steven,
I'm sorry that it took so long to get back to you. I have
read your manuscript. You sure do have writing ability.
But unfortunately, I must pass on your manuscript. This
is a subjective opinion.
   Best wishes
   Sincerely, Gina Heft

 I didn't want to hear any made-up excuses or be complimented on my remarkable achievement. I wanted to sell a book! Literary agents needed to feel confident they could earn ten thousand dollars on a book before deciding to represent a writer. Without a literary agent, I had to promote my book on my own, putting myself in a difficult position.

 It took me six years, pitching to agents at the writing conference until I found an agent willing to "coach" me. After editing and rewriting a children's book for a month, trying to impress the agent, she agreed to represent me. I received an email from the agent one Sunday late in the evening, offering me a contact. Mom was asleep in her bedroom when I typed back "yes" to the agent. I emailed my friends, telling them about getting an agent. When Mom woke up around eleven to put me to bed, I had an enormous smile on my face and said, "We have an agent!"

 "Oh, that's nice dear," Mom replied, yawning at me.

 I drank my root beer, watching Sports Center, dreaming of becoming a known author. It was a moment of victory for me. I kept moving forward spending the rest of the summer, rewriting several children's books for my agent. Then my agent decided that she wanted me to write a middle grade manuscript. I spent one year writing, rewriting, and editing a middle grade book. I worked late at night while Mom slept in bed.

 Back in our Minneapolis hotel room Mom placed the manual wheelchair in between the two beds before she struggled to roll me over, and then lifted me. She somehow managed to maneuver down the narrow gap, separating the beds, carrying me in her arms toward the wheelchair. Mom twisted and pivoted me in a sitting posture in the chair

My muscles became rigid making my entire body thrust forward and causing my butt to begin to slide out of the wheelchair's seat.

She kept her right hand on my shoulder to prevent me from falling. Mom squeezed herself between the bed and the wheelchair, trying to get behind me to pull me up in the seat. She grabbed the loops of my blue jeans, yanking me back in the chair.

I held myself so tight preventing her from pulling me back.

"Relax, Steven!"

I hated to hear those two words from my mother's mouth. It always makes me feel angry.

She kept tugging on the loops before finally managing to scoot my rear end into the seat. Mom then positioned my rear end. She walked in front of me. Mom untwisted the wrinkles in my jeans to prevent welts from developing on my legs and buttocks. She retrieved the urinal from the hotel room's bathroom cabinet. Mom unzipped my fly and pulled down my underwear. She held the urinal and then aimed my penis inside of the plastic container.

I urinated.

Mom emptied and rinsed the urinal before putting it back in the cabinet. She zipped my zipper and fastened the button on top. Then Mom buckled my seat belt before taking off my navy-blue pajama top. Mom shaved the stubble off my face. After shaving me, she took out a clean Wisconsin Badger shirt from a suitcase and put it on me. "We'll put on a new shirt when we go to the theater tonight."

"Okay." Reams of drool from my red moist fat lower lip dampened Bucky the Badger on my T-shirt.

She picked up my shoes from a chair and knelt on the floor to put them on me. Mom stood up again. She retrieved a tube of A and D ointment from a gray duffel bag lying underneath the table. Mom applied the ointment to my dry and calloused right hand. She pushed me toward the television.

"What do you want on TV?" Mom asked.

"I don't know. I'm not usually up this early."

I normally didn't get up until around ten. My bedtime routine was to stay up late and watch reruns from the seventies and eighties when TV producers actually hired writers. After the television timer clicked off around 1:30 a.m., I masturbated. Then

I lay awake in the dark for a couple of hours, thinking about what to write the next afternoon before falling asleep. I tossed and turned several times, dozing off for a short period before my tense muscles woke me up. Around three I kicked off the blankets. I wished to have a sexual relationship with a woman. In my dream, I imagined being straddled by a brunette with firm round breasts. I watched her put me inside of her, enjoying being "ridden" several times, until I couldn't ejaculate. Then I asked her to masturbate. It was just fantasy, offering an escape from my reclusive life until I called Mom to put the blankets back on me.

She covered me again.

Another half an hour passed before I fall asleep, dreaming vivid dreams again. I dream about being a big-time author with an agent. My favorite dream was about living in Beaver River, helping Amanda and Dan teach their classes. The ultimate fantasy was speaking about my young adult manuscript to Amanda's English classes. I pictured sitting in front of a classroom teaching students, or tutoring a student in how to write. Then I saw myself critiquing papers for Dan and Amanda. It gave me enjoyment, imagining teaching Amanda's class, and starting an argument with her about how to critique a persuasion paper.

"Steven, your critique of the purpose sentence of the persuasion paper is too harsh," Amanda said in the dream.

"I know what I'm doing! I'm the author!"

"Well, I'm the English teacher!"

I laughed.

"I got you going," I said, smiling at Amanda.

She hit me over the head with a pointer.

Chapter Six

FAMILY HOLIDAYS AND SPORTS

Back in the hotel room Mom pointed the remote control at the television. She stared at me and asked, "What channel do you want? I have to go out," Mom said.

"I want ESPN," I answered.

She looked up the channel to ESPN on the hotel's television guide, and then she punched the number into the remote control. Mom grabbed a brown cigarette case from her purse.

"I'll be back," she said, opening the door.

I jumped when the door clicked shut. Then I sat, drooling and watching College Football Game Day with Reese Davis, Keith Herbstreet, and Lee Corso. I yelled, "Go smoke your cigarettes! You're killing yourself, Mother!"

She always smoked. Mom smoked more as she grew older, until it became a habit. She spent all of her time caring for me.

When Mom and I drove to Milwaukee to visit my sister, Lynn, Mom always left early. She made an excuse like she didn't have the vision to drive in the dark or the Weather Channel predicted snow, starting that evening. The minute she pulled out of the upper-middle-class development where Lynn lived with her husband and two daughters Mom lit up a cigarette, filling the van with cigarette smoke. Mom cracked the driver's-side window open, cutting down the amount of smoke I inhaled, but letting in the cold air. She kept rolling the window up and down every ten minutes to smoke.

I wondered what my sister, brother-in-law, nieces, and in-laws thought when Mom left early for home when all I wanted to do was watch my nieces play, and play peek-a-boo with them. I suspected Lynn knew Mom needed to smoke, but I believed that my sister blamed me for our leaving early, so I could watch a football or basketball game. Growing up it seemed to her I needed to watch every Packers, Badgers, and Bucks game.

Sports provided me with an escape; but the older I became, watching basketball and football simply gave me a break from writing.

Once, while Mom and I were visiting, Lynn asked what game I wanted to watch.

I sat drooling in my manual wheelchair as I watched Lexie and Courtney play House. Dora Explorer was on television.

"This," I said.

"Are you sure?" Lynn asked.

"Yeah." I had a big smile on my face.

"Something is wrong with you, I swear," Lynn said.

It seemed wrong to leave without singing "Happy Birthday" to Lexie or eating birthday cake. My brother-in-law's family believed in having a party. It lasted five hours and with lots drinking, and it took several minutes to open each present. His family opened Christmas presents in the early morning hours on Christmas Eve. It was my brother-in-law's parents' custom to have a large traditional dinner, drink, play cards, and sing Christmas carols.

This approach to celebrating holidays and birthdays made me envious. For our meal on Christmas Eve, Mom fixed shrimp, crackers, cheese, potato soup, and Mom's homemade cookies. I watched Sports Center's top-ten sports highlights of the year, as I sat there muttering to myself, "Next year will be better!"

Mom arrived in the living room with a smile on her face. She carried a couple of presents that I knew were for me.

"Get yours in the closet." I pointed my eyes to the big closet near the door
.

Mom retrieved a paper bag from the coat closet.

After buying her present at the technical college's gift shop on the last day I worked, I brought it home in a paper bag already wrapped. I asked Mom to put the gift away until Christmas to keep it a surprise.

Mom held a red present in front of me.

I stretched out my right hand to accept it. My long damp fingers raked against the wrapping paper. I yanked off the white ribbon, and then my fingers ripped open a seam in the paper.

Ashes and Coal ran out to investigate the rustling noise. Ashes batted the ribbon from my fingers. Coal watched Mom finish opening the gift for me.

"Thank you for the Packer shirt."

"You're welcome." Mom smiled at me.

She helped me open the second present. When we were done, Mom held out a nice navy-blue dress shirt. She smiled and said, "You need a new dress shirt for the writing conference in April."

My eyes lit up.

"Thank you. I can't wait to be with writers and see my friends. Amanda says that I will be known one day!" I said. Every year at the conference I met writers who became friends. We would email after the conference, networking and talking late at night with a writer. Writers kept me company in the evening.

"I will pay for the writing conference. That's part of your Christmas gift," Mom said.

"That is what I want! The conference is everything to me! Now open yours, Mom."

She picked up the bag, and pulled out the unwrapped gift. The receipt fell out onto the floor. Mom looked at the Christmas ornament saying, "It's lovely, Steven. Thank you very much!"

She hugged me and then hung the glass-ball ornament on the miniature Christmas tree on top of the television cabinet.

Ashes and Coal stared at the new glass ornament twitching their tails. Ashes sat still but ready to take a running leap at the tree. Coal groomed himself on the rug.

Ashes took off racing throughout the house. Coal licked his paws as he purred at me.

"Merry Christmas, guys. I love you." I looked at my cats.

I spent the rest of the evening watching Sports Center as I looked forward to seeing my nieces, brothers-in-law, and Lynn the next day. Soon I fell asleep dreaming about teasing my nieces and sister.

On Christmas Day Mom decided to leave when she saw Lexie, Courtney, Mark, and Lynn fall asleep on the leather tan sofa after opening their presents. She drove back home with the radio on playing endless Christmas songs. Mom arrived back to our condo before three p.m.

I wondered why Mom had driven to Milwaukee only for a couple of hours. After getting home, I had cookies, ice cream, and a mug of iced tea with my twenty milligrams of Baclofen. I then watched the Celtics Lakers game followed by the Spurs

Mavericks game, and the Trail Blazers Warriors game. The rest of the evening was spent watching basketball alone for the next six hours while I listened to my neighbor's doors open and close.

Back at the hotel the hotel's door opened. Mom entered the room.

I smelled the stale foul cigarette odor on my mother's breath immediately. In an instant, I read the scroll on the television screen, announcing the Badgers Wildcats game could be seen on ESPNU.

"I'm back. There's a Subway across the street. Do you want a sub?"

"Yeah, I'll take a combo, potato chips, and a Coke. Get ESPNU!"

"What?" Mom asked.

"ESPNU, Mom!"

"What is ESPNU? Are you sure that's the channel you want?" Mom asked.

"Yes!"

She picked up the TV Guide from the dresser drawer to look up ESPNU. Mom switched the station to ESPNU. She smiled and said, "I don't know how you know what channel all of your games are on."

I didn't need a TV Guide. I knew just by reading ESPN scrolls and Sports Illustrated. I knew the national and local sports schedules to keep track on what games I wanted to see, which was easy since I only watched sports.

After Mom saw the Badgers helmets and the purple Northwestern uniforms playing in Camp Randall on a sunny Saturday afternoon she said, "Well, I'll go get our lunch. What do you want on your sub?"

"I will take pickles, olives, onions, tomatoes, lettuce on Parmesan," I said.

She repeated my order back to me.

"Yeah," I tell Mom.

"I will be back." Mom goes out the door again.

I watched the game and it made me realize how lucky I was to have expanded cable to see my Badgers play. At home Mom only had the basic cable channels. I couldn't see all of the games now ever since the Big Ten and the NFL started to broadcast games on pay-per-view cable channels in order to generate more revenue. I understood Mom's fixed income didn't afford luxuries like expanded cable, but it still made me angry. What the NFL commissioner and university presidents seemed to have forgotten was that many low-income people, like the physically disabled, practically live to see their teams play. I looked forward each week to seeing my Packers play on television, or traveling to Lambeau Field to witness one of Aaron Rodgers' last-second victories. When the Packers win, it makes my week. Being at a Packers game and seeing the Packers win made my month. The Packers held a wheelchair-lottery and allowed the wheelchair bound to choose a game or two from the home schedules. The wheelchair-ticket lottery did cost sixty dollars a ticket plus another ticket for a companion that didn't include the forty for parking. Then food and gas added to the game day's expenses. My face lit up when I won a ticket in the lottery. It gave me something to look forward to, but then the Packers decided to make wheelchair tickets season tickets. The tradition of attending a Packers game was eliminated for me since I couldn't afford to purchase tickets to eight Packers games. It used to be that Mac and I would buy tickets to Bucks games, but the average of one NBA ticket was only one hundred dollars. Most people, including the physically disabled, don't have three hundred dollars sitting around to spend on a game. My prediction was in the next ten years, ticket prices and pay-per-view sports channels would probably make me have to choose what I watch in the future.

I watched the Badgers score two touchdowns in the first quarter before Mom arrived. At the beginning of the second quarter, she opened the door carrying a cardboard tray with two sodas. In her right hand dangled the cellophane bag containing two sandwiches and potato-chip bags. Mom set the food down on the table. She then pushed me over to the food. Mom gave me my ten milligrams of Baclofen, a medication to relax my tense muscles before she fed me.

We ate in silence, watching the Wildcats score a touchdown in the final minutes of the first half. I finished lunch during halftime.

She wiped my mouth and lap. "Will that satisfy you?"

"Yeah." I burped loudly and smiled at Mom.

I let out a loud burp again and passed gas when Mom pushed me back in front of the television.

She retrieved a peppermint from my backpack and placed the candy into my mouth.

For an unknown medical reason that doctors haven't yet been able to explain, sucking on a peppermint helps keep my food down after I eat. If I didn't have candy, I might throw up my entire meal. I didn't plan on eating at all before going to the play since I might gag when I became excited. Sometimes when my body is extra tight or I'm very excited I will throw up.

I always cut back on what I ate when on a trip, or at an evening event. Then I learned that by eating less on special occasions, it helped prevent an embarrassing situation. I didn't want to be out in public, having diarrhea running down my legs, making me smell like an ant house.

Mom disappeared to smoke again, but she returned after the Badgers scored another touchdown, reeking of stale tobacco. She took out crossword puzzles, Word Seek puzzles, a pen, and a couple of colored pencils from her purse before lying down on her bed.

The Badgers scored another touchdown and a field goal to put the game away. I watched the entire game.

After the Badgers game ended, I looked at Mom, saying, "I'll take ABC."

She rose and walked to the television. Mom glanced at the TV directory to find the correct channel. She tapped the buttons on the remote control, turning the station to ABC.

"Is this what you want?" Mom asked.

I saw the plain white uniforms, lining up against the scarlet and gray uniforms. But when I saw the horseshoe stadium and the Buckeye stickers on the gray helmets, I smiled. "Yeah, it's Penn State and Ohio State."

"Well, I'm going to take a nap."

"Okay," I said.

Mom lay down on the bed. Within minutes, she fell asleep and started to snore.

It was back to being alone. I thought about the contestants on TV reality shows who become lonesome in a matter of only a few days. It made me laugh when the constants received a chance to talk to their loved ones after spending a month in seclusion. The contestants cried after not hearing or seeing their relatives for a short period. I didn't understand why the contestants became so emotional considering a month without seeing a loved one isn't very long.

I didn't see Mac my cousin, Jill, and Amanda for months at a time. The last time Dan visited me was ten years ago. After Lynn divorced my brother-in-law, Mark, my sister "disowned" Mom and me. She felt that Mom had lied about me being on my own since I started to receive home health care in the mornings. This was because Mom could no longer lift me out of bed. But I wasn't ready to move out and Mom didn't push me. For seven years, I had morning care attendants from ten to one Mom took care of me the rest of the day. I didn't need much care. It was easy to stay with Mom, writing and enjoying my simple life. Lynn decided to go on with her life without us, not answering emails or phone calls. Holidays came and went without a word from Lynn. Mom and I sent Christmas presents and birthday presents to my nieces but didn't receive a thank-you. It hurt. But life went on. Each April, I met Amanda at the mall near my house when she brought her high school Forensics team to compete at the State Finals in Madison. In my mind, Amanda had become my sister. I even called her my sister when we were in college and in the ensuing years the word sister became a nickname for Amanda. When Mom heard me say sister, she always had to think twice. Was I talking about Lynn or Amanda? But Amanda meant everything to me. I spent the two hours at the mall talking, teasing, and running over Amanda's feet in my electric wheelchair before she gathered up her students and headed to their hotel.

"Are they good?" I asked.

"I did my job. You can only do so much, as you know. It's up to them now."

I soon realized no matter how much effort I put into preparing the students for competition, ultimately it is the students' willingness to put the time in that determines how they will perform.

A few of Amanda's students walked up to her. A tall blonde with wavy hair and crystal blue eyes asked, "Is this Steven?"

"Yes," Amanda nodded

The students smiled. They didn't stare at my continuous drooling.

The blonde said, "Mrs. Tilley talks about you all of the time. Mrs. Tilley tells us about the crazy emails that you send her. You get Mr. Strong to play jokes on Mrs. Tilley, like taking her gummy-bear jar and not refilling it. We saw the video of you using Morse code to write. You're amazing! But Mrs. Tilley is making us write journal entries about what we watched. You're a good writer."

"Thank you. Mrs. Tilley is mean for giving you homework," I laughed.

Her students didn't understand my speech. Amanda glanced at her wristwatch.

"Steven, Steven, what I'm going to do with you! It's time for me to gather up the troops."

"Tell Dan 'Hi' and tell him to visit. I miss you! I will email you on Monday. After I email New York about a book, I will email you. One day, Amanda!" I exclaimed. Amanda knew how badly I wanted a book to be published.

"It's going to happen, you know. Keep at it, Steven! Bye. Email me." Amanda waved goodbye to me as she left.

I lived for moments like the ones where I see Amanda, or helped teach Forensics at the technical college. There were other moments I hated, such as visiting Doctor Johnson at the Rehabilitation Clinic. I knew what she was going to say after she tried stretching my tight legs apart.

When she stopped stretching my legs, she always said, "Well, Steven. Your tone has increased. Maybe we should increase your dose of Baclofen, or have a Baclofen pump installed like we've talked about in the past."

"No!!!" I shouted.

When I told people that I didn't want to get another power chair, it left them scratching their heads. I always laughed when I saw the TV commercial advertising motor scooters to the elderly. It made me want to pull my hair out when the bald spokesman with bifocals smiled and said, "Increase your mobility at little cost or no cost to you."

I hated the long process of ordering a new electric wheelchair. My wheelchair vendor, Henry Noble, came over to the house with brochures and a demo chair that fit a seat for me.

It's a New Life! Mom is Gone

When Mom transferred me from my manual wheelchair to the demo, I slipped out of her arms. Henry grabbed my legs and helped Mom put me into the power chair, but the rigidity in my body prevented me from sitting upright in the electric wheelchair. After Henry transferred me back to the manual chair, he looked at me and said, "I can't order a new chair until I can properly fit you Steven, you need to take more relaxation medication before we can proceed further."

Doctor Johnson prescribed more Baclofen and Valium. It made me sleepy to relax my muscles. When it didn't work, she injected Botox into my four hamstrings to reduce the muscle tension in my legs. It allowed Henry to mold a seat for me, but my hamstrings hurt from injections for a couple of weeks, making it painful to sit.

I never complained to my Mom about being in pain, but I emailed Amanda about the pain and she called Mom to tell her.

The seat didn't work. I watched Henry, Doctor Johnson, Mom, and a physical therapist argue over the proper seat for me.

I just sat there as I pictured how to put their concerns into a novel one day. It didn't matter to me as I remembered that there was always something wrong when I received a new electric wheelchair, like a defective head array that made the chair inoperable. Henry had to order a new head array which took another month to get.

"Well, what do you think, Steven?" Doctor Johnson asked.

I yawned, giving him a dazed look and said, "Whatever! Just get it here by April! That's all that I care about."

"What's so important about April?" asked the overweight gray-haired physical therapist.

"I go to the writing conference at the university! Agents from New York and LA are there! Writers and authors come from all over the USA! That's what I live for. One day, I will have an agent! New York, New York, here I come!" I said, and my eyes lit up as I talked about the writing conference.

"I have already promised you, Steven that the chair will be here by April." Henry looked at me.

"Just do it, Henry!" I gave Henry a stern stare.

Doctor Johnson said, "We want you to have the perfect seat for your new wheelchair."

I laughed, knowing the perfect seat didn't exist. It reminded me of writers, attempting to write the next bestseller. It didn't matter to me whether the seat was perfect or not. I knew the electric wheelchair wasn't going to be used much when I sat at the computer writing. Henry, Doctor Johnson, and the physical therapist didn't take into account my daily life: writing. I forgot about the wheelchair as months passed before the new electric wheelchair arrived. Time kept slipping away as I imagined a better process of attaining a power chair.

Baclofen made me sleepy. I fell asleep after supper due to the increased dose of the muscle relaxation medication. It didn't help when I saw other physically disabled people fell asleep at Lambeau Field during a Packers game in their wheelchairs. I needed to be alert when I wrote, critiqued and taught, and wanted to be awake during the evenings to watch basketball or football.

A Baclofen pump meant having surgery. A catheter attached to a pump delivered Baclofen to the central nervous system. Catheters break at the most inopportune times. The device sat at the lower chest, and with my uncontrollable hand movements and drooling, it would be more probable to get infections that caused more problems. Having a pump didn't guarantee my tense muscles would relax more. I didn't want to be in and out of the hospital, becoming a vegetable like a Cerebral palsy acquaintance of mine who had a Baclofen pump installed. Every five years the Baclofen pump needed to be replaced, requiring another surgery, and a two-day stay in the hospital. I didn't have time to lie around for something that, in the end, might not work, causing me endless pain. My friend's surgery was botched when the surgeon placed the pump in the wrong area. It took months to heal and required him to stay in a nursing home for six months. He spent his life as a disability advocate for years, helping to make disabled people independent; but after the surgery he felt sorry for himself, calling himself a "selfish cripple."

He took more medications, an addict thanks to these powerful drugs, making himself into an ornery brat, abusing his care workers, and sleeping at the mall all day, urinating in his pants. One of my biggest fears was becoming a vegetable, I knew some disabled people who spend their days eating, sleeping, and watching TV, but I wanted more out of life.

My time was valuable. I didn't want to be him. All that I wanted to do was to write each day to leave a legacy to show people that I did have something to contribute to society. When I would no longer have the physical ability or the mental capability to write, I wanted to die. When Mom passed away, I worked with my lawyer, rewriting my will that stated I didn't want to be resuscitated or have a feeding tube. I named my cousin, Mac, and a college classmate, Pam, as my executors of my will a couple of weeks after Mom had passed.

Doctor Johnson said, "Steven, we want you around for the next twenty years. You're a great asset to have around."

Why in the hell would I not want to live for the coming decades? I had set out to educate people about the mountains of red tape, rules, and procedures that threatened a severely physically disabled person's independence. Waiting for another new electric wheelchair gnawed deep inside me each time I needed a new chair.

I viewed myself at a voice for the severely physically disabled who were unfairly discriminated by some people. All the barriers that faced I didn't stop me. My friends kept pushing me forward when I dealt with the highs and the lows, but mostly the latter of being an author.

Mac took Mom and me to the Guthrie Theater once to see *Dear Old Friends*. The musical was about three college classmates. One friend dreamt of becoming a writer. He wanted to be a known author someday, but doubted himself His two friends witnessed the writer's struggles from writing his first book to finally publishing a couple of books. He eventually became a best-selling author. The author's classmates saw him doing a TV interview on the Today Show, saw his books in hard covers prominently displayed in bookstore windows, and had to call his agent to visit him. His book became a best-seller overnight and he was in demand, doing interviews and book signings at bookstores across the country. The three friends reminisced about the writer's hard path to fame after he sat writing day after day and received what seemed like endless rejections from publishers and agents. The news media didn't recognize his first three books. Yet he managed to land an agent to represent him. The writer never forgot the powerful influence and strength his two dear old friends gave him to pursue his dream.

Mac watched me laugh, smile, and cry during the performance. It scared Mac when he saw me bawl at the end of the play.

When the performance ended, I stared at Mom with tears, running down my face. I yelled, "It's us. Ma!!!"

Chapter Seven

I AM AN ADULT NOW!

Dan gets me up early helping me into my manual wheelchair to write, read, and answer emails. After opening CoWriter and Outlook Express, I exit Mouse Mode before I use Shift Tab to highlight the first email. I start reading the condolences. "Are you okay?" Amanda asks, looking at me. I smile at her with tears in my eyes. "We're here." Dan tells me. I say in a soft voice, "I'm okay." My two friends disappear into the small kitchen, leaving me alone to write.

I start replying to emails. My agent writes, "What can I do?"

My answer is, "Just get me published!"

Then I notify one of my Mom's college classmates about her passing. The first line of the email read:

Dear Sally,
Mom passed away Saturday evening after a brief illness.

The second Mom passes, I become an adult, making big decisions like who is going to care for me and where to live.

I have no idea what going is happen to me, but in a matter of few weeks I would learn what Mac meant as I dealt with my family, my agent, case managers, care attendants, and roommates.

"I can't believe that you two are here."

"We made you a promise that we would make sure you were taken care, if something ever happened to your Mom, didn't we?" Amanda asks.

"Yeah but," I say.

Amanda pops a red grape into my mouth. Droplets of grape juice drip from my mouth the second after my teeth split the grape open.

Dan sits at the table eating potato chips and a bologna sandwich. Between mouthfuls Dan says, "That's what friends are for. And we'll always be here. We need the author around. Right, Amanda?"

"Promise is a promise!" Amanda says.

I remembered the day when they made this promise to me. Amanda, Dan, and I sat in a circle with eight other English students, during Professor Watson's Creative Writing class, critiquing short stories. While each student's composition was being critiqued, he or she had to remain silent. I loved talking to my classmates and professors about writing. It drove me nuts not able being to say a word when the class critiqued my composition.

Professor Watson read aloud the first paragraphs of each student's story before the critiquing started. Watson read the opening paragraphs of my composition in a soft voice. He read:

A Writer's Fear
By Steven Salmon

I sat at the computer all afternoon, writing a novel. Letters formed into words, turning to sentences and then slowly becoming paragraphs, pages, chapters, and a novel. I wondered if being a writer was worth it. Being a writer meant spending days alone. The possibility of becoming a hermit, like a vegetable watching TV all day in an institution and not being able to write, scared me. I worried about living in an institution if something ever happened to my mother.

But my biggest fear was losing my two best college friends after I graduate. People come in and out of my life. My classmates would probably disappear leaving...

In an instant, I hit a red buddy button on my tray and drove out of the classroom. I vanished.

Amanda and Dan looked at Professor Watson and asked, "May we be excused?"

"Yes. Go talk to him!" Professor Watson replied.

Amanda found me, crying in a corner by the elevator. She gazed into my teary eyes and said, "We'll always be there for you. We promise."

Dan appeared. He heard the promise being made to me. Putting his right hand on my shoulder he said, "That's right; we'll always be there for you."

I stopped crying to look at my friends as saliva poured from my big red pouting lips. "Yeah, but. You'll forget about me. You'll move on and have families," I said.

What hurt me the most was when a friend didn't even say goodbye. I distanced myself from people I considered to be friends to avoid a broken heart. It was my wish to have life-long friends, but I never believed I could.

"We'll never forget you," Amanda said.

"No matter where we are or how far apart we are when you need us, we'll come running. That's a promise!" Dan said.

Amanda shook her head. My friends never forgot their promise to me they made years ago.

Back in my house, I turn my head toward Amanda, opening my mouth wide waiting for her to put another red grape in.

She pops a grape into my large mouth. Amanda yells when I almost bit her finger. "Hey, you almost got my finger," Amanda shouts.

I laugh.

It doesn't seem real to have my two best friends here, helping me. It feels surreal, as if I'm dreaming one of my vivid morning dreams. I don't want to wake up from the dream of having Amanda and Dan providing care, but I know I need to confront reality. I want to go back to sleep and pretend Mom's death hasn't happened.

A sleepy Mac staggers into the living room from the winding narrow hallway in his gray Packers sweat pants and blue Nike T-shirt. He stops beside an antique maple drawer to rub his eyes. Mac scowls at me before he heads over to the computer. He fires up the computer without asking me and then sits down in a captain chair. He plays with the mouse. Mac taps his right hand against his knee saying, "Hey, this puppy is slow! I'll update for you today."

"No, Gravel!!!" I shout.

The last time Mac updated my computer he paralyzed the Morse code software, making it inoperable.

I didn't have a computer for two weeks, making me unbearable to live with until Mom hunted down an occupational therapist from the Computer Disabilities Alliance who came to disable the update. The delicate Morse code program didn't exist anymore. The occupational therapist warned me to not have any one install updates on my computer, or risk destroying the system permanently.

Mac starts to play around with the computer.

"I said no. Gravel! Dan, talk to him," I say.

"Maybe you better leave the computer alone," Dan says to Mac.

Amanda feeds me another grape saying, "Let's be safe and not sorry."

Mac stares at my two friends and says, "I'm just checking out ESPN.com, for Christ sakes!" "We need to back up my documents on the memory stick," I say.

"Where is it?" Mac asks.

"I don't know." I shrugged my shoulders.

"What do you mean that you don't know?" Mac asks. "You're an adult now!"

I feel bewildered, confused and lost, but Mac is right: I am an adult now. While I take time to mourn in brief moments, I have no choice but to be an adult. The only thing that I have is to keep moving forward. Mac stands up and walks to a small table next to the recliner. He picks up the remote control and starts to click through the channels. Mac turns around to ask, "Hey, writer! Do you have ESPN News?" "No, Gravel," I say.

"You need it to stay current with the sports news," Mac says. I laugh, watching Mac as he changes channels, stopping to critique a local newscast, and rating the different female anchors on their sexual appearance and their commentary. Amanda wants to cover her ears. Dan and I laugh at Mac demeaning and rude sexual comments.

"Barb Lantz on channel seven has big boobs but no ass. But Jennifer More from channel four has no ass, but nice breasts. But that new redhead on channel eight has it all! Look at those boobs, pussy, and ass. You know what they say about redheads and their red crotches; they keep begging for more. I wouldn't mind giving her a ride!" Mac says.

"Are you through?" asks Amanda.

It's a New Life! Mom is Gone

"Yeah, Amanda I am. I want tea, please," I say.

She stands up to give me my drink and then raises the glass mug to my mouth and puts the straw in between my lips.

Mac sits back down at the computer.

I drain the six ounces of iced tea in seconds.

Amanda grabs the empty saucer with the grape stems from the table. She also takes the mug and the dish back to the kitchen.

"Hey, Favre is thinking about not retiring again in order to play for the Vikings," Mac says.

Drool flows from my mouth onto my blue dress shirt. I begin to cough.

"Who cares?" I ask.

My coughing increases, but Amanda rushes in with a peppermint. Usually when my jaws start to lock open, this makes me gag. When Amanda puts the candy in my mouth, I stop gagging.

I grow tired of hearing the speculation about the annual potential of Brett Favre's retirement. Brett always vacillates about whether to retire or continue playing.

It reminds me about what happened after I graduated from college. Special Needs college advisors, social workers, some of my professors, and even a few of my relatives told me to go back to school. But Amanda and Dan always believed in our dream, reminding me that going back to school doesn't accomplish anything because I already have writing talent. I always listen to my friends. For years now when summer ends, I feel an urge to return to college. After nine years of college, I want to become a writer—and don't intend to become an unemployed physically disabled Rhodes Scholar.

The system, disability advocates, and our society don't know what to do with people who have severe physical disabilities *and* an education. The only answer the system has had for people like me is to keep going to school. What I learned is that people don't hire or pay the physically disabled a wage. Some people believe the physically disabled are hopeless cripples who should be content watching TV all day. Going to school for years keeps the severely physically disabled out in the community, giving them something productive to do. I know a higher education needs to be used, and returning to college will never achieve my goal of becoming an author.

I hold the precious moments of school I've had with Amanda and Dan.

"Well, I guess you'll have to move to Minneapolis to live with me," Mac says. Mac tilts the captain chair back to grab Ashes' tail saying, "You can bring your cats. I promise I won't make kitty-cat stew out of them." Mac lives next to an old Chinese woman who likes to cook Asian dishes. He believes she spices her food with dog or cat meat. Mac liked to joke with Mom and me that cats kept disappearing in his neighborhood; and his neighbor, Mama Yang, seemed to eat well on her low Social Security income.

"I can't live with you, Gravel. You drive me nuts."

Mac lives in a two-story old craftsmen house in a gang-ridden neighborhood where drug dealers and hookers hang out on the street corners. Stairs lead up to a porch. More steps and the home's narrow doorways unfortunately make the house inaccessible for wheelchairs. The old furnace doesn't provide enough heat to keep the rickety house warm.

I imagined the daily arguments if Mac and I did live together. The stubbornness of two cousins living in such close quarters would threaten to destroy our relationship. The older I became, the quieter I needed my surroundings to be to help me write. Being a writer meant sitting at the computer day after day.

Mac does what he wants when he wants. He doesn't think living with me means giving up his freedom.

"Then where you are going to live?" Mac asks.

"I don't know yet. I have been working on it, you know! My case manager Becky will have answers," I say.

Amanda looks at Mac, "I have called Becky, as well as his nurse from the Long-term Living Coalition (LLC). They'll be here tomorrow with Steven's care team."

"That should have been done a long time ago," Mac says, giving me a dead stare. "But we should have done more to help your Mom," Mac tells me, with a guilty sounding voice.

"Keep moving forward, Gravel," I say to him. The past is gone and I need positive thoughts now, not guilt. My sheltered world has been turned upside-down. Moving forward helps me keep thinking ahead to the next big decision or problem facing me.

Dan returns to the open living room. He glances at his wristwatch, "We better get going, Steven, if you want to make your 12:30 class."

"You can't be serious, Steven! You're going to school the day after your mother dies," Mac says.

I spin the electric wheelchair in a circle, stopping in front of Mac. A bubble of drool pops from my mouth. "No! I'm going to work! I don't go to school! I have a job! We're going! Bye, Gravel," I say. Then I turn the wheelchair toward the door, looking at Dan and Amanda. "Let's go!" I yell.

When Dan holds the door open, I drive the chair out into the foyer.

Amanda follows me out.

"It's not a job, Dumb Dweeb! All you do is sit," Mac says.

My job requires me to listen to students' speeches. Then, the next day, I email my critiques to the students. Sometimes I don't like how the Forensics instructor, Cathy Chestnut, runs the class. Most of her Forensics students participate in the college's theater productions, and during those productions she allows students to skip class. At times students don't show up for class. My job is coming to an end when the semester ends due to a lack of students' involvement. I feel a commitment to finish my job, and Cathy is a great friend of mine. She always attends the writing conference with me. I don't like losing my job. But I do my best, working about thirty days a year, listening to speeches. It gives me an activity to do outside of the house. I decided to become a full-time writer. My career is taking more of my time with edits and rewrites. I look forward to being a writer, but I will miss being with the students.

Once, when Cathy had jury duty, I taught class. I didn't believe the students would stick around to practice their speeches. At first the students ignored me, but when I shouted, "Okay, you people," the class stopped chitchatting. One by one the students performed their interpretive speeches in front of me.

When the last student finished, I said, "You guys are good. I will email you critiques tomorrow. You can go."

I drove down the long hallway, smiling to myself thinking about what I would say in my email to Amanda and Dan the next day.

Steven B. Salmon

English teachers,
I taught class yesterday. The students stayed and
listened. I even said, "You people." Well, I have
critiquing to do. A teacher's work is never done. Steven

While writing a critique to a student, a new-message icon appears in the computer screen's lower right-hand corner. I finished my email to the student, but all the while I wondered what Amanda's or Dan's reply said. I opened the new message.

That's cool. Now try teaching teenagers. Amanda

I laugh before continuing with the critiques. Receiving an email from Beaver River made my day.

I carefully drive the electric wheelchair down the bus's ramp. Gazing at the three-story brick technical building makes me feel proud about being an employee. I race the wheelchair toward the main entrance.

Amanda and Dan run ahead of me to catch the doors. Dan holds the first door open, and Amanda opens the second door. She raises her voice at me when I pass her. "Don't you dare run over my feet!"

I run the electric wheelchair past the display cases, showing off the technical college's sports trophies, the gymnasium, and the theater, all the while laughing at Amanda. I maneuver up a steep ramp, scraping my left hand against the brick wall, cruising around the Welcome Center; but I stop for a second to bring in my outstretched hands to avoid knocking down or accidentally grabbing a student's food tray. I forget how many times my finger or hand can catch a tray, spilling food and drinks everywhere. Students aren't paying any attention to where they walk when I rocket down the center of the hall. I laugh when I hear Amanda yell, "Slow down." When I drive, I don't wait for anyone unless the person specifically asks me to stop.

I wait at the cafeteria for Amanda and Dan to catch up with me before driving past the different Student Life Center offices. I smell pizza and soft pretzels coming out of the Recreation Center. Rock music blares away. Stopping at the bakery, I drool at the cookies, pies, cakes, and cupcakes, waiting for my turn to order.

I jump when a tall man with black curly hair standing behind a glass counter in a white apron asks, "What will it be today, Steven?"

My eyes roam the counter. I want all of it, but instead say, "I want apple pie and cherry pie."

"Is that all?"

"Yeah," I say.

The baker grabs two plastic containers, one containing a slice of apple and the other cherry pie. He then puts the containers in a white paper bag. The man walks around the counter to put it in my backpack hanging on the back on the wheelchair. He walks in front of me saying, "You're all set! Have a good day."

"Thank you. I will," I say.

I head across the main hallway to the three elevators, wait for an elevator to open, and then I zip in before students either fill the elevator or the doors closes.

Dan and Amanda hop into the elevator. The doors shut. Dan asks, "What floor?"

"Three," I reply.

He presses the button, making the elevator jerk up. Dan rubs his stomach, looking at Amanda saying, "Boy, I wouldn't mind working here! You get free food!"

My part-time job at the technical college allows me some perks like receiving free baked goods from the bakery and free tickets to see theater productions. Some of the Theater Department staff members remember me from when I attended college many years ago. They know of my dream to become a writer and admire my dedication to my writing. The theater chairman, Stan Cham hired me as a Forensics teaching assistant after my second book was published. The staff quickly learned I don't go out much except help out with the Forensics team. The theater staff knew I have a sweet tooth after seeing my white paper bags in my backpack after each class. When I offer to pay for the treats and theater tickets, they told me to use my "pocket change" on something I really want.

I raise my right hand to hit the power control switch from forward to reverse. I wait for the elevator doors to open before I lean my head back into the head array to backup the chair. When I clear the elevator, I stop a few feet away from the elevator to knock my hand on the control button and power the wheelchair forward.

To avoid running over students' legs and feet, I run the chair down the center of the wide corridor. Students sit with their backs leaning against lockers, leaving very little room to negotiate a power chair past the mess of human lower appendages.

Most of the time students do make room for me to pass unless they are studying, talking, or asleep. When I don't have enough space or a student doesn't move out of the way, I say loudly, "Beep, beep, beep," making them move. I run the electric wheelchair past science labs, lecture halls, computer labs, and the Art Department.

Then I drive by offices and classrooms before I turn into a doorway. My outstretched arms bang against the blue metal door frame and the door itself when I enter the classroom.

Cathy smiles at me. She continues teaching, giving directions to the class about when and where to meet for the Forensics competition in Minneapolis.

I park horizontally beside a long empty table next to the door as I hit my hand against the power switch to turn off the chair.

When Cathy finishes, she faces me saying, "I didn't expect you to come today. I'm so sorry about your mother."

"I know. But I needed to get out and be with my people. Amanda and Dan are here. I want them to see the duo," I say.

"Welcome to our class. Please make yourself comfortable. I have heard a lot about you, especially Amanda. That's all he ever talks about is Amanda except for the Packers and writing," Cathy says to Amanda.

Amanda and Dan sit next to me. Amanda gives me a dirty look saying, "I can just imagine what crazy stuff about me he said to you."

Cathy motions Steve and Jessie to bring their black notebooks with them.

Steve stands behind Jessie, cradling his book in his right hand and in front of him.

Jessie appears to be pointing at an easel. She paints broad strokes, using an imaginary paintbrush in her left hand while she holds the black book in front of her. Jessie hunches over, in a sitting position, painting alone.

It's a New Life! Mom is Gone

Steve has gone out of the classroom and closes the door behind him. A minute later he reenters the room and starts to read out loud the passage as he bumps into Emily.

Paul walked into the Art classroom. He came behind Emily, admiring her, painting when Paul bumped into her manual wheelchair.

Emily's body jerked, making her drop the paintbrush. A streak of green ruined the perfect blue skies.

"Look where you're going, will you!" Emily shouted.

"I'm sorry, Emily. I'll clean it up. I didn't mean to scare you," Paul said.

"Don't you know by now that you never startle me when I paint?" Emily asked.

He picked up her brush and handed it to her.

"I said that I was sorry!" Paul replied.

She watched him use a damp paper towel to clean up the spatters of green paint from the floor.

"Well, it doesn't matter because my painting sucks! I'm an awful painter. I give up!" Emily exclaimed.

In the novel by John Black, A Different Painter *is about two college classmates who are Art majors. Paul admires Emily's paintings and her artistic ability to paint beautiful picturesque partings. He doesn't believe Emily wants to give up her dream of becoming a painter. Paul challenges her to keep her dream alive.*

"You've to be kidding, right? You not painting... that will be the day!" Paul said.

"I'm serious, Paul! Being a painter is a lonely life. I don't have much talent to make it," Emily told him.

"Sure you do!" Paul replied. He looked at her painting of a giant maple tree, standing in the middle of a soybean field. The huge tree's limbs seemed to hang over an acre of soybeans. A lone cardinal sung from a top branch, singing at the perfect blue sky.

"Your painting reminded me of Walt Whitman's poem from 'The Leaves of Grass' about a giant maple, standing alone. You know, you'll never be alone," Paul said.

"Why?" Emily asked.

"Because you'll always have me, and I won't let you give up your dream," Paul said.

"I don't know, if I..." Emily stopped herself from finishing her sentence.

Tears start to roll down my cheeks. "It's us." I say to Amanda and Dan before I start to cry. My two friends stand up.

Amanda and Dan walk around the table to console me. Amanda hugs me in her arms. Dan pats my shoulder. Amanda and Dan say, "We know, we know, Steven. We'll be there for you! You're surrounded by friends."

Cathy, Amanda, Dan, and the rest of the class gather in a circle, standing in front of me, trying to comfort me.

Chapter Eight

THE BULLY

I had become more isolated in recent years. My opportunities to be independent were limited. When I drove my electric wheelchair outside, people called often the police or police officers stopped me.

"Are you lost?" a policeman once asked.

"No."

"You shouldn't be out this far, you know. Your battery is running low! Maybe you should turn home," the policeman told me.

I kept driving the chair, laughing and drooling at the officer, who was following, me in the patrol car.

"Where do you live?" the policeman asked.

I tried to tell the officer, but the policeman didn't understand me.

"Stop," the officer said, hopping out of the cruiser. He located my home address with my phone number on a piece of a paper attached with duct taped to the back of the wheelchair. The officer retrieved his cell phone from his pants and called Mom.

I kept motoring along trying to annoy the officer, who kept asking if I am all right.

The policeman hung up.

"You're good to go! Enjoy your ride! It's a nice day for it!"

I continued driving the wheelchair, watching and laughing as the policeman drove away. I love the freedom of being in my wheelchair and enjoying the outdoors, but I have to be vigilant of my surroundings. When I rode past young boys, I learned to ignore their snickering, name calling, and rude questions. I don't have to worry about girls taunting me. When I drove past girls, they just stared and laughed at me before going on their merry way.

Once I drove the power chair across the empty city park while I gazed at the rush-hour traffic as it whizzed past on an avenue when a boy approached on a mountain bike. I saw a baseball bat stuck in between the handlebars.

The boy rode his red bicycle up to me. He pedaled right beside the wheelchair and stared at my drooling and uncontrollable body movements. The boy yelled, "Hey, fucking cripple retard. Do you know that you're drooling?!"

I kept driving toward the softball diamond and shelter as I tried to ignore the boy.

"You're a disgusting dolt. Why can't you even swallow? Do you wear a diaper? Do you pee in a bottle? Who shaves you? Do you work? You probably can't even count to three! Answer me!" the boy exclaimed.

I kept moving forward, ignoring him.

"Stop," the boy shouted.

I didn't stop.

"I said to stop! I want your money. I'm going to use my baseball bat to bust your head and break your wheelchair," the boy demanded.

I heard "Thacks" of baseball bats, echoing from the minor-league baseball team in the nearby ballpark. After putting the chair in "High" gear, I turned back to the duck pond. I spat spittle at the boy.

He said, wiping away the spit from his face, "How dare you! You ungrateful son of a bitch! I know what you're up to. I'm going to race ahead and close it before you can get there!"

The boy raced to the green wire mesh gate to shut it.

"Na, na, na! You think that you're so smart! You're coming with me, and I'm going to kill you!" the boy told me.

"Fuck you!" I yelled.

I rammed my chair into the gate, making it shake open, creating a space for me to enter. After spinning around, I headed down the path toward the grandstand.

The boy followed me yelling, "Hey, idiot! Can't you read the sign? It says 'No Trespassing!'"

When I reached the batting cage, I yelled at a couple of players, "Help, help, help me! He wants to kill me! I'm in danger!"

The two baseball players, wearing Oakland Athletics uniforms, stared at me in the power chair, foaming at the mouth.

"He's my brother, George. Come, George, we should be getting home before father whips us," the mean boy said to the baseball players.

A tall baseball player with freckles and blond hair stood while he leaned on his baseball bat as he stared at me. He chewed on sunflower seeds before saying, "I think that you better go with your brother."

A large bubble of drool popped from my gaping mouth. My arms and legs began to thrash. I composed myself just enough to understand my difficult speech since it was live or die. I am scared.

"He isn't my brother. I don't know him. He wants to kill me! My Dad is dead. I go to Madison College. I live with my mother. I'm not going with him. Call my Mom!" I said in a firm voice.

The second player, with a red goatee and a stout short build said, "I'm going to check into this. Something isn't right."

The ball player jumped over a low green fence and asked me for my phone number. He smiled at me. "Be right back."

I watched the player walk to a white cinder-block shelter to the pay phone. Then I felt relief as sweat poured down my armpits and back. A gentle cool breeze blew and helped me to relax a bit.

The tall player stood by the batting cage while he watched his teammates take swings, but the boy slipped away.

The first player returned. He patted me on the shoulder, making me jump saying, "I'm sorry, I didn't mean to scare you. Your mom is coming."

"Hey, he's telling the truth." said the goatee player, pointing to me. "Where's the boy?"

The tall player looked around. He shrugged his shoulders and said, "Gone, I guess."

The boy may have escaped, but Mom and I knew the bully might have hurt or murdered me.

I felt I had been raped by the incident. It took away the innocence of being able to enjoy the beautiful outdoors alone which most everyone enjoys. I loved being outside, watching squirrels dart up trees, listening to a babbling brook, and feeling free on a perfect sunny summer day without anyone near. But the bully took all that away. It took time for me to overcome my fears of driving the electric wheelchair outside alone. I was always looking over my shoulder. The second that I saw any boy I put the chair on "High" gear, speeding away in the opposite direction from the boy or hiding in a hidden spot.

The incident scared Mom. She knew I needed to be independent and wanted me to be independent. Mom dreaded sitting at home all afternoon while she waited for my safe return. She hated receiving phone calls or knocks at the door from police officers, questioning her about my mental state, and whether it was all right for me to be out alone. However, it usually meant the wheelchair's battery was dead or a part had broken. Mom didn't like driving around town in the van, looking for me, wondering what had happened to me now. She usually found me stuck someplace, like under a tree next to a park shelter or in the middle of a softball diamond in the hot glaring sun. After locating me, Mom then needed to push the heavy electric wheelchair to where she had parked the van. When Mom reached the van, she lugged the power chair up the ramp and into the van. Then when she returned home Mom repeated the same process to get me in the house, exhausting her.

When I used the electric wheelchair, Mom transferred me in the morning and I sat in the electric wheelchair until Mom put me to bed. I used to spend all day in the chair, but stopped using the electric wheelchair for driving outside alone. I got tired of dealing with do-gooders and the police stopping me or worrying about being attacked. I stopped asking to go out since I knew Mom would sit at home smoking, waiting for me to return, or waiting for the phone to ring. I only used the electric wheelchair when I worked at the technical college, attended the writing conference, and when Amanda brought her Forensics team to the mall. I figured I only used the twenty-eight-thousand-dollars electric wheelchair about thirty days a year.

Chapter Nine

WHAT NOW?

During the last years of Mom's life, she made it hard for me to go anywhere. Mom made comments to my attendants like, "I can't wait until the writing conference is over." Anything different from Mom's normal schedule and she became confused.

My friends Stan and Bob would visit at times, but it became a hassle to invite people over. Her response when a person came over was, "You didn't tell me that someone was coming." I needed people, but I just accepted being a hermit, only writing for my agent and emailing my friends. My people kept me alive, but I wanted more than just writing. I wanted my own place and to have sex. Mom controlled everything, including my SSI. We argued a lot the last year of Mom's life. Part of me wanted to move out but I didn't want to hurt Mom. I didn't realize how isolated I was until Mom passed away. That's when my world changed overnight.

Everything changes in one night when Mom passes. I'm outside with my family in the early evening. It feels strange sitting by the condominium's swimming pool, watching my nieces Lexie and Courtney swimming with their cousins, Rita and Kelly. I have my nieces now. Five years have passed since I saw them last, but my mind is spinning in circles. Helicopters fly above the perfect blue sky. I feel guilty not answering or writing emails I should be writing. I sit by my cousin Jill looking at the sky, thinking about Mom and my book.

Amanda takes Dan to the bus depot to return to Beaver River but not before talking to me alone. I ask them again, "Can I do this?"

Dan says, "Yes, you can and you have to!"

Then Amanda tells me, "I expect nothing but the best from you."

Tears roll down my cheeks and I say, "I will keep moving forward, I promise." My two best friends nod before Amanda replies, "And listen to your family—especially to Lynn! I mean it, Steven! And be patient with people!"

Dan says, "I echo that! You have to roll with things now." Amanda nods before stepping back, giving Dan time to say goodbye to me.

I say, "Okay, I will try."

"What are the things that you want to do now other than the obvious?" Dan asks, making me laugh. "Okay, other than s-e-x. What things do you want to do? Where do want to you go?" Dan asks. "You can do anything now! The world beckons, Steven!"

I had never thought about the bigger picture before saying, "I want to go to New York and Beaver River."

Dan asks, "Where else? You can sit on the beach in Florida or California."

"The Grand Canyon, but I want to visit you," I tell Dan.

"There's nothing special about Beaver River." Dan says.

"It has you and Amanda. I'm coming to Beaver River! One day we will make it. I miss you." I say with tears in my eyes.

"You can come, Steven, and I'll visit you more, I promise. Everything is at your fingertips. Anything is possible now, like being a New York author. Go out there and grab it. Well, I have to go, Steven." He looks at his wristwatch. "You need to email Larry Watson. He cares, you know. Bye, Steven." Dan walks out of the door. I nod, remembering my writing professor, Larry Watson from the University of Wisconsin-Stevens Point for a moment before crying again.

I'll be back. Be good to Lynn," Amanda tells me.

I tried to reach out to Lynn several times over the past five years. I feel like there are times when she didn't answer my emails and I gave up. Sometimes when I emailed Lynn in the past, she might reply with a long email about how hard her life was, but I didn't want to hear it.

My life had become more secluded. My Forensics teaching-assistant job gave me a way out of the house. The three hundred dollars I earned from Forensics and critiquing papers for Stan was my only spending money. Half of my spending money was spent on my nieces, and I saved the rest for book publicity. Every couple of days Mom went to the store to buy cigarettes, and

It's a New Life! Mom is Gone

she would purchase too much food that was wasted, but I wanted to use money to build my career.

I knew that life was hard for Lynn, being a single parent with two girls, having a career, paying a mortgage, and being a mother. My brother-in-law had an alcohol problem that made him verbally abusive at times, but living with my sister wasn't easy either. Lynn could be petty, impatient, and stubborn (like me) at times. She was passionate, sensitive, and caring. I loved her dearly, but we had grown apart, being two very independent people. What I wanted was to be an uncle to my nieces.

My cousin Jill taught chemistry and trigonometry in Racine. I haven't seen her for eight years. Jill was my favorite cousin. She listened to me, unlike Mac. Years ago, I decided to make Jill my guardian in the event Mom was unable to care for me or passed away. When Mom developed signs of forgetfulness, anxiety, and paranoia, I made Jill my second power of attorney. My friend Stan took me to the lawyer's office. Four months later, Mom passed away; and if I hadn't made Jill my second guardian, I would have become a ward of the state. I enjoyed having Jill back in my life.

I saw Mac maybe once a year when he visited his mother in West Bend, Wisconsin. We might go to a Bucks game, but he worked as a news director in Minneapolis now. He wanted and needed to spend time with his family, including his nieces. Time flew as we pursued our careers. It seemed that time stood still now.

When I sit by the swimming pool the next morning after Mom's death and watch my nieces swimming. Mac and Lynn are on their smart phones, working their jobs. I look at Jill, sitting in a lawn chair, and say, "I have to go back and get working. I need to send some emails. My agent might want me. My career doesn't stop."

"Steven, you need to take a break," Jill tells me.

"I have a career!" I exclaim, thinking about the post that I want to write for my blog, email I need to send to Dan, and all the emails I need to answer. My career and my vast network of friends keep me busy. People know who I am after I wrote an article for a Milwaukee newspaper about Governor Walker's plan to privatize long-term care. I had over eleven million hits on my website a week after the article appears. Mom created a known author with her sacrifice and dedication to me. People are finally

73

reading what I write. "Gravel, let's go! The author needs to write!" I shout.

Mac says, "I'm busy!"

"I said *now!*" I tell him.

"You need to be polite to people, especially to your caregivers. And say please and thank you!" Lynn says.

I do give my care attendants respect, but I am the boss. My two male care attendants at the time of Mom's passing were very reliable. One was a RN and always arrived ten minutes early. Rick showed up ready to work, but Mom didn't let any attendants, including him, do much except take care of me during their three-hour morning shift. My other attendant, Ken, was a gentle soul who needed to be guided by me at times. Ken could be twenty minutes late since he rode his bicycle to work, but Ken always came. He would return when I took the electric wheelchair out somewhere and then need to be transferred to the manual wheelchair or bed. I was managing my care, but Mom was confused about who was working a shift.

"Don't tell me how to treat my care attendants! I treat them well. Where were you for five years?" I ask Lynn in a high tone of voice.

"I knew that was coming! I guess I deserve it." Lynn bawls in Jill's arms.

"Let's go, shithead!" Mac exclaims, grabbing my manual wheelchair and pushing it outside near the swimming pool. He pushes me up a steep hill as we head to my condominium. Mac jabs me in the neck with his fingers and says, "You're so stupid. You need your sister now. There was no will. The house is unsanitary. We're cleaning it up so you can have a care staff here. You'll apologize to Lynn and thank her."

I don't care, but I say, "Okay."

"Now where are you going to live?" Mac asks, maneuvering the manual wheelchair through the series of doors to enter the condominium.

I want to live here, but Lynn found a fifty-thousand-dollar mortgage on the house hidden underneath the pile of papers on the kitchen counter. My mind is full of everything that's happening all at once. I've had to make so many decisions in a very short period of time.

My only answer to Mac's question is, "Becky knows what to do."

He sets me up at the computer and leaves me to work.

Emails flood my inbox from friends, asking if there is anything that they can do. Friends like Cathy, Bob, and Stan drop in to see me. I cry the second I see any of my friends. It surprises Mac, Jill, and Lynn how many friends I have. I overhear Mac asking Lynn, "Who are these people?" I laugh at my cousin's response

Lynn whispers to Mac, "I think that they're college instructors and former instructors from the technical college. You know, Steven has a way with people. He can get people to open up to him, and some people just open up to Steven for some reason."

She remembers me telling her once about a young woman who just walked up to me one afternoon when I sat on the pier, watching sailboats sail on Lake Mendota on a clear day.

I sat on the edge of the pier as I drooled and stared at the sparkling blue water while I watched the incoming waves beat against the rough rocks when a pretty brunette approached. My muscles began to tense up. I thought she would probably drag me back to the boat launch to protect me for my safety.

Instead she stood next to me, placing her hand on my shoulder. The woman smiled looked at me and asked, "It's a lovely day to be outside, isn't it? My name is Sarah. What's your name?"

"Steven."

"It's a pleasure to meet you, Steven. I have MS. You have Cerebral palsy," Sarah said.

"Yeah," I replied.

"I just wanted to say hello. I want to be a doctor," Sarah said.

I told her about my dream of becoming an author to educate people about Cerebral palsy.

Dreams happen at the most inopportune times. After opening my inbox, I see an email from my agent with the subject line: sent to Harper Collins. I click on the email and read the message.

Steven B. Salmon

Dear Steven,
The president of Harper Collins and eight other
publishers in New York are reading your middle-grade
book. Good luck. I will be in touch. Stasia

I take a deep breath and cry before creating a new message to Dan. It doesn't seem real to me. My dream is coming true, but Mom has passed. I am tapping away when Lynn dashes into the condominium with a scowl. She doesn't acknowledge me as she runs into the bathroom to change her clothes. Jill walks in next and says, "I want you to apologize to your sister right now."

"Okay, I will," I tell her. My nieces run throughout the condominium, filling the living room with their laughter and shouts. I continue to tap away among the noise. My nieces may see Uncle Steven write, cry and collapse in people's arms for moments, but they also see me continue to write. Lynn reenters the living room wearing a dress. I look at my sister and say, "I'm sorry Lynn."

She nods before walking out of the door saying, "Get writing the obituary because the funeral home wants it. Forward it to me when it is done." My sister and I are a team. I say, "Okay, I'm on it!"

I have so many emotions going through my mind right now.

Lynn is meeting a lawyer to set up a Special Needs trust fund for my inheritance and will also run errands. I finish writing the obituary, forwarding it to Lynn to send to the funeral home. I also reread the email my agent sent, telling me that my book is in New York at Harper Collins. I break down in the arms of Jill and Mac. "It's real! The dream is true," I exclaim, bawling my eyes out.

It feels like one of my wild imagination dreams, but it is true. That night I can't sleep. Welcome to being an adult! Shit flies!

My mind is overloaded with all that is going on. I am definitely an adult now with all these new responsibilities. It feels like I'm tumbling off a waterfall and the color of the water is shit. I don't see where I'm going, but I roll with it! My people are just an email away. Each email from my friends makes me cry.

It's a New Life! Mom is Gone

I continue tapping my second language. Writing in Morse code allows me to communicate anything to anyone in the world and is my main language. After forwarding the obituary to Lynn, the intercom buzzes and Jill answers it. I'm in my writing zone, zoning out the world around me when a middle-aged woman with bushy blonde hair pulls up a chair next to me.

"I'm Flo Bates from Integration Residences Services. Pleased to meet you. I'm sorry for your loss," Flo says, smiling at me.

"Hi," I say, still writing away and not comprehending what Flo wants. The words "sorry for your loss" sting when I hear the phrase from people. It leaves me numb since I know I will be on my own in a few days after my family goes home. Mom is gone! It feels empty without her, but yet I'm surrounded with love. I see it but am too numb and busy to let the love sink in.

Mac comes to take off the head array when the intercom buzzes again. Flo pushes me to the dining room table. Jill answers it again. Mac is watching Sports Center from the sofa, biting his fingernails. I look at Flo and say, "I'm an author!"

She picks up my business card from the table.

My case manager, Becky Bucda, and my nurse, Tara Pearson, walk into the dining room. Becky hugs me. Tara pats my shoulder and says, "Please accept my condolences."

I tell them, "My book is in New York. Harper Collins and nine publishers are reading it!" Then I break down, crying.

"It's a bittersweet moment," Tara says.

Flo, Tara, Becky, Jill, and I gather around the table. Folders are opened and papers suddenly appear.

Mac saunters over before sitting down next to me. He has a yellow spiral notebook and a pen to take notes.

It's time to go back to work, but before I do, I say, "It's my fault! I should have moved out years ago, but I was too embarrassed to have someone else clean me up at night."

"Oh, Honey. She did that because she loved you," Flo tells me.

"Absolutely," Becky says.

"You shouldn't be guilty of anything. It's not your fault," Tara tells me.

I thought about the countless times that I heard my professors, instructors, friends, and relatives say I took Mom for granted. I heard numerous people tell me what a fortunate man I was to have Mom caring for me. Sentences echoed in my mind, but it didn't register like, "Do you know how lucky you are to have her?" or "Your mother is a saint." It embarrassed me when Amanda or Mac told me that I didn't really appreciate how much Mom did for me. When I reached my late thirties, I saw the sacrifice and complete devotion she gave each day in order for me to pursue my dreams.

Lynn and Mac knew about my bowel-movement problem but didn't talk about it. Mac learned about my problem when he opened his grandmother's bathroom door once to say good night. He saw me, lying naked on my stomach on a black rug while my father, Patrick cleaned my dirty rear end. Mac ran out of the house on the verge of being sick to his stomach. But he became used to it. He took Mom and me to spend a weekend in Chicago to see the Cubs play at Wrigley Field and to see the sights. Mac pushed me in my manual wheelchair down Michigan Avenue in the early evening. A horse, pulling a white carriage, passed us and the smell of excrement filled the air. Mac asked laughing, "Is that you dumping or the horse?"

"Oh, shut up, Mac," I said, feeling annoyed by his remark since I hadn't taken a "dump" in my pants.

"It's not your fault," Becky says, reassuring me as we talk in the condominium

When I hear and read the phrase "It's not your fault" from my family and friends, including my agent, it stops me from blaming myself.

I nod with tears in my eyes. After I laugh, I keep moving onward and say, "Okay, Becky. Let's move on."

Becky says to Mac and Jill, "As you know, a couple of months ago Steven started the process of moving out on his own but it didn't work out."

My cousins nod to Becky. I met a potential roommate and his sister, showing they already knew, two months before Mom passed away. Mom was in denial about me becoming independent. Rod had MS and was a writer. He had written a couple of articles in college. Rod spent his days at the mall going to the movies. He lived in a group home, but his only request was for our new apartment to be near the mall, allowing him to drive his electric wheelchair to the mall and avoid taking the bus. The mall was

Rod's "home" just like the writing conference was for me. It seemed like the perfect match, but the problem was that Rod had asthma and was allergic to cats.

I have always had a cat. It wasn't possible for me to live without a cat. My cats kept me company during those long eight- or ten-hour days of writing when Mom was asleep. Writing could be stressful at times, and I needed my cats to relax when I had a deadline or my agent wanted something. My Mom didn't know what I was doing half of the time. I even offered to surrender the cats to live with Rod. After I tried to ignore Ashes and Coal for a day, I realized I needed them. I emailed my case manager, Becky, to start looking for another roommate.

Becky continues, "Flo is from Integration Residence Services, which places consumers in homes in the community. Steven is eligible right now. Flo can tell us more."

"Steven, you would live in your own house with a couple of roommates, sharing expenses and a twenty-four-seven staff. You're in charge of everything from where to live to what you want to eat. You will always have someone with you now. Will you hire Integration?" Flo asks me.

I don't like having a person with me all of the time. It drives me nuts that Mac, Lynn, and Jill wouldn't leave me alone for an hour. I need and want to be alone in order to write. Mac was always reading what I wrote in emails. Now people were invading my space, but I kept on writing wishing to be alone. I look at Flo and ask, "Can I have my cats?"

"Of course, Honey," Flo answers, rubbing my arm. "Our staff will take good care of you, I promise."

Before I can talk, Mac yells, "What about these emails that Steven sends us about care attendants having miscarriages, being in car accidents, borrowing money for gas or cigarettes, asking for rides, being scared of cats, injuring their backs, taking people to the hospital, disappearing to Missouri for three days, showing up late or not at all, taking a week off after an attendant cut themselves with a razor, an unauthorized attendant, giving Steven a sponge bath, and an attendant, showing up to be trained without having an interview with him. And On-Call workers who don't do anything because they're injured requiring Mary to do everything. What about that!"

"Our staff is mostly RNs and nursing students. We take good care of our consumers," Flo tells Mac. She looks at me, "I promise you, Sweetie, that we'll take the best care of you. What do you say?"

I think for a moment. This is my first big decision! I'm in control now but I don't want to be. I'm an adult now. Shit is flying everywhere now! After I take a deep breath, I tell Flo, "You're hired."

Flo hugs me and says, "That's wonderful, Steven."

The shuffle of paperwork commences. Becky asks, "Steven, where's your rubber stamp?"

"On my desk by the light is the stamp," I tell Becky.

She gets up and retrieves the stamp. The stamping begins.

I don't know to what feel. I am lost, but I make the decision. I know that my people are behind me. But still I'm alone without Mom. Time keeps moving fast.

Mac asks, "Who cooks and grocery shops?"

"The staff will, but Steven decides what he eats, when he eats and gets up and goes to bed. Steven can go to bed at four in the morning if he wants," says Flo.

I laugh, imagining myself, writing in the early morning hours, but that would soon become a reality as I chase my career and manage own my care.

Flo asks, "Steven, what's your daily routine?"

I see Flo pick up a pen and a steno pad as she waits for me to talk. Then I tell Flo my typical day. "I don't get up until ten. Then I have a bed sponge bath. I get dressed and get up. Then I go pee. After brushing my teeth, I put on my shoes. I shave every other day. Then I have lunch. I have ten milligrams of Baclofen with iced tea. I eat potato chips, nachos or fruit. After I eat, I have to have a peppermint to keep my food down. Doctors don't know why, but it works. Then I read for two hours and an attendant turns pages. An author needs to read! Then I write for four hours. Don't bother me when I write. I go pee before I eat. At five I eat supper. My supper needs to be well balanced with vegetables, meat, fruit and bread. I eat everything! I love steak, watermelon, apples, and ice cream! Then I have candy, like a lemon drop to suck on while I watch TV. It takes a half an hour for me to digest my food. I write again for four more hours. At eleven I have a root beer with thirty milligrams of Baclofen. My body needs an hour to settle the root beer before I go to bed. Then I can go to bed. A person will have to clean me up. Then I watch TV in my room. Someone will have to set the TV timer. Someday, I will go to New York! I live an author's life. My people know that I will make it. I have to because of Mom," I say before I have an emotional break down as I burst into tears.

Flo, Tara, Becky, Mac, and Jill embrace me. Becky tells me, "We are here, Steven."

After a moment, I say, "I'm okay."

All of them sit back down. Becky asks Flo, "When can we look at houses?"

Flo says, looking her tablet, "Next week I'll email you soon with a couple of days and times. Give me a day or two to assemble a staff for Steven."

Becky says, "Sounds good to me."

Mac says, "I will be here for another day."

Jill replies, "Lynn and I go home tonight. I'm going to Seattle to visit my sister in three days for a couple of weeks. Lynn has a deadline to meet for a major work project by next week, but Amanda will be here."

"My staff will be here tomorrow to train," Flo tells us.

Tara, Becky, and Flo gather their materials and start to leave. The minute everyone stands up, I start to feel alone. I'm scared like shit. Soon I will be on my own for the first time of my life. I have no choice now but to grow up. Life with Mom is no more. It's time to be a man. My people believe that I can do this and I will. A tear rolls down my cheek, but I collect myself. After my care team leaves, I go back to the computer, tapping Morse code, creating a new life. My people are just an email away.

Steven B. Salmon

Chapter Ten

CARE ATTENDANTS

The next day my care attendant, Ken, feeds me lunch.

"For the love of God, what are we going to do with you?" asks Mac. He sits at the computer and slaps his leg with his hands. Mac turns toward me, saying, "Vick is out for the season—that fucks up my fantasy football team, The Angry Assassins! I'm totally screwed!"

I jump when Mac yells, banging my right knee on the dining room table. I sit reading a novel.

Mac keeps slapping his legs. He stares at me. "You're getting jumpier; you know that, McFly. You should take more relaxation medication."

I ignore my cousin's comment and the stupid nickname he sometimes calls me, and instead keep looking at the book. "Okay," I say to Ken a signal for him to turn the page.

He stands up before sauntering to the table to turn a page for me.

"We need to get you a page turner! But they are so expensive!" Mac says.

Page turners cost about three to six thousand dollars. Mom didn't want to purchase one before she knew it worked for me. Specialized medical technology companies don't allow people to try out adaptive devices before purchasing. Mom and I lived on a fixed income, but when Mac visits us he sits at the computer, searching for page turners on the Internet and always finding the same adaptive aides.

Ken flips a page in between washing the dishes in the kitchen. There is a lot more for Ken and Rick to do now that Mom is gone. No more sitting around for my attendants.

"I will check the Net for page turners," Mac says, walking back to the computer. "You need to be reading newspapers, not books! You need to know what's going on in the world around you!"

He sits at the computer, reading the *Sports Illustrated* website.

I don't try to argue. CNN is always on during the day when Mac is around.

For an hour I read as Ken cleans and Mac plays fantasy football. After my stomach is settled, I say, "Ken, I will write." I don't want to work, but I have emails to write and answer.

Ken unlocks the brakes and pushes the manual wheelchair to my office. He puts the head array in place on the back of the wheelchair and plugs it into the USB Port. I take over the computer and say, "Thank you, Ken."

"I'll be back at four to feed you supper," Ken answers.

"Okay," I say, watching him push his bicycle out of the front door. I listen to his bike as he maneuvers awkwardly through the doors and out of the condominium.

Before I get writing, Mac tells me, "Please write an email to Aunt May. She's worried about you. Please express your condolences to her about her sister. Remember, it isn't all about you."

"Okay," I tell Mac. I feel the burden of all these expectations on me from my friends and family, but I'm grieving. Time ticks away. I don't like being told that I am selfish, but I know I can be. Then I realize that I must do the best that I can to show to my people that I will succeed with my new life.

I start to write an email to Aunt May. Aunt May is the monarch of the family. Her strong and devout Mormon faith makes her cherish family ties. But when she received my Christmas letter, it hurt her more than it did my other relatives.

Some of my relatives like Aunt May, whom I had always admired—never forgave me. It didn't help that Mom forgot to send my apology letters. I admitted my mistake, but there was still a lot of the truth in the letter. It was when I read Aunt May's email that she sent after Christmas that I realized my error.

Her email read:

Steven,
Your Christmas letter really hurt your family. You said that you didn't need us anymore. Maybe that's why you don't receive any "visitors." And now you want us to come because you are having trouble with your

attendants. You're just spoiled. You didn't even apologize to us, and now you want us to come. That's selfish. Your dreams are just dreams. You will never be successful. People don't care, and don't want to read about problems of the disabled anyway. A "writing career" is just a fantasy that will never happen. What about your poor mother, sacrificing her life for you? What a waste! You're a failure. You need to grow up and become a man. It doesn't matter. Eventually you will end up living with one of your relatives anyways. Stop feeling sorry for yourself. Aunt May

Aunt May's email hurt me. She used to make homemade apple pies after I earned high grades in junior high school, achieving a spot on the honor roll. Aunt May kept encouraging me in high school to continue getting good marks. She witnessed my strong determination to attend college and become a writer. Aunt May was proud of me, accomplishing my dreams against the tremendous odds, but she developed serious health problems (arthritis, and having a colostomy bag), making it difficult for her to get out of the house. She worried about Mom's health as her health declined. Aunt May wondered what would happen to me when Mom wasn't able or capable to care for me.

I write an email to Aunt May. It reads:

Dear Aunt May,
Please accept my condolences. Mom is Mom. There is no one like Mom. She created a known author. There are over twelve million hits on my website. I have a book in New York right now. It's all because of Mom. I hired a care agency today. In a couple of weeks, I will live with roommates and a staff twenty-four-seven. It won't be easy, but my friends believe that I can do this, including my agent. Well, Aunt May I have things to do. Please don't worry about me. I'm a man now. Amanda and Dan know that I will make it. I have too much to live for. Love, Steven

I continue emailing others when the intercom buzzes making me jump. Mac answers the door. I'm in my writing zone, blocking out my surroundings, concentrating on my writing, when a woman wearing a purple dress and a white turban sits down next to me. I think that she is a gypsy from outer space.

"Hi, I'm Karo," the woman says in an African accent.

"Hi," I say, thinking that she is one those care attendants who I will have to fire in a week or who quits. In the past I have trouble with my care attendants.

Three years before Mom had her heart attack, I hired two male care attendants named Lou and Jim.

Lou's reserved and easy-going personality appealed to me. He lived in the same neighborhood. Lou liked the outdoors, sports, and reading. One morning he walked into my bedroom with his smile, "Hi, Steven."

"Did you sleep well?" Lou asked.

"Yeah, I did," I said.

"Did you?" I asked.

"I did. Thanks for asking," Lou replied.

Lou walked to the bedroom's window. Before he opened the blinds, he said, "Let there be light."

I blinked my eyes when the light flooded the room.

He bathed and dressed me. Lou asked, "Did you see that grand slam hit by Ryan Braun in the top of the eleventh with two outs, and the count was full against the Cardinals?"

"No. I watched the Spurs and the Lakers. Double overtime," I replied.

"You and your basketball; that's all you watch on TV," Lou said.

Lou and I laughed. He fed me at the dining room table. We talked about politics, current affairs, and our dreams. Lou asked me during lunch one day, "What's your dream that you want to accomplish yet that you haven't accomplished?"

"Get an agent," I said, laughing before gagging on a potato chip.

He wiped the chewed white bits from my shirt and mouth with a damp washrag and said, "I already know that!"

"But what's one thing you've wanted to do but haven't?" Lou asked.

My eyes darted checking for Mom before I answered, but she was busy watching television in her bedroom. "Have sex," I said.

It's a New Life! Mom is Gone

"Every guy needs to experience intercourse at least once in his life. There's nothing like it!" Lou tells me.

Mom forbids me to have sex. During the last couple of years of Mom's life, sex becomes an extreme want in my mind. I crave sex. One of my care attendants offered to have her boyfriend take me a strip club, but I knew that if Mom found out she would stop me from going anywhere. I wanted to go but didn't. Mom caught me surfing porn websites at night and had those sites blocked. I felt like a caged lion on the prowl.

I had always wanted to have sex, and I did have a couple of opportunities to have intercourse, but my modesty kept me from sharing my love with a woman. I pondered why I tried to hide my physical problems from women but I didn't yet have an answer.

I wondered why Lou worked as a care attendant.

Lou liked to help people. He worked as a missionary in the Soviet Union, teaching English to children, helping to dig wells, and teaching erosion techniques to farmers. Lou helped me cut and paste press releases to the local news media after the release of the second book. He also assisted me in shopping for a birthday cake, birthday card, and a Mother's Day card for Mom.

On Memorial Day Lou helped his own mother clean out her fish ponds on her farm. He lugged five-gallon plastic buckets around all day as he carried slime water from the ponds. When he returned home, his back started to ache. Lou lay in bed, unable to stand up. He had a slipped disc that required surgery and months of physical therapy. Lou became disabled. Lou could no longer work for me.

I felt sorry for Lou. It reassured me to know I could count on Lou to be on time unlike my other care attendant, Jim.

Jim arrived on time his first week of work. Then he started to show up late, or miss a day a week. Jim only worked for me three days a week for three hours from ten to one, but he always seemed to have an excuse for his tardiness.

He would walk into my bedroom between 11:30 a.m. or 12:30 p.m. and say, "I'm sorry I'm late, dude. But I have a sleep disorder and have chronic back pain. I just fell asleep around eight o'clock. That's why I'm late. I promise that it won't happen again!"

I would lay awake in the mornings when Jim worked at his other job waiting and wondering when or if he would arrive; the worry made my muscles tight. I held my urine for so long that when I tried to go it took me a while before my muscles relaxed and I could urinate.

Jim tried to tell me what to do, what to eat, and what I should do. He wanted to be my advocate, but I just needed a care attendant.

One morning I lay awake in bed, staring at the red digits flashing on the clock radio, watching time pass. Where in the hell was Jim, I wondered? I had papers to critique and wanted to email Amanda. Each day I set goals to achieve. Time ticked until the telephone rang at eleven. I waited for Mom to hang up before yelling, "Ma."

Mom opened my bedroom door and said, "Jim will be late. He overslept. I will get you up so you can watch the NCAA basketball tournament."

She dressed me, transferred me to the wheelchair, took me to the bathroom, put on my shoes, groomed me, and fed me my lunch.

When he finally arrived, I was watching basketball while I sucked on my peppermint. Jim walked in around 12:30 p.m.

"Sorry, I'm late. Is there anything that I can do for you?" Jim asked.

"No," I said.

Sticky drool dribbled onto the floor. I stared at the television, ignoring Jim, who was sitting at the dining room's table as he made calls on his cell phone.

A half hour passed before Jim stood up and said, "I'm going if you don't need anything."

I stared at the television, watching basketball, relaxing, and getting mentally prepared for the writing conference, which was coming up the next weekend.

Then, the day after the conference Tara, my nurse made her fifty-day scheduled visit. I wanted to get up to email Amanda, Dan, and agents I had met at the conference, but Jim hadn't yet arrived.

"Is he always this late?" Tara asked.

"I don't like it! I'm busy! Agents, Tara! I can't wait all of the time for him. I'm working," I said.

The intercom buzzed. Mom ran to let Jim in.

"I will give him a warning today after his shift here. If this keeps up, I want you to email me, and we will terminate him," Tara said.

"Okay," I replied.

"Always email me when you have a problem with an attendant. I'm here to help you," Tara told me

Jim walked into the bedroom. "You have to email me about the conference this afternoon. I can't wait to hear everything."

Jim didn't really try to understand my speech. He made comments like, "It has to be hard to be misunderstood all of the time." "What you need is an augmentative communication device." or "I feel sorry for you, dude."

I didn't want pity or to be told what to do. For lunch, I ate some grapes with iced tea after reading a couple of articles, giving my stomach time to digest my food before getting set up on the computer. I didn't care that Jim wanted me to read, allowing him to earn his three hours for that day. Then I emailed Tara to fire Jim. After I emailed Amanda and Dan to tell them about the conference, I emailed agents and sent out manuscripts as I dreamt of becoming a known author. When I read an email from Amanda, telling me to keep up the good work, a tear rolled down my cheek. One day, people will know who I am.

Jim received his two-week notice, but he didn't say anything about being terminated until after the first week had passed. He set me at my desk with Mom, who was keeping a close eye on how Jim put me on the computer.

I started to write when Jim hit the plus-sign button, stopping me from writing.

"I don't really understand why I'm being let go. I really like it here. Please reconsider," Jim replied.

"We'll think about it," said Mom.

"I appreciate it," Jim said, smiling at Mom.

I grumbled, knowing that Mom had left the door open for Jim to stay. Then I emailed Tara and Amanda about what Jim did. I decided to take control of the situation during the next shift Jim worked and after I urinated. After I was up, I waited for Jim to empty and rinse the urinal.

"Sit down, Jim," I said.

He sat down on the edge of the bed.

"I like you. But it isn't working out. You're a good worker. It's like agents. Agents say I'm a good writer. But I'm not good enough for them. I'm sorry," I said.   "I don't understand," Jim replied, looking at me.

"Agents say I'm a good writer. But I'm not good enough. People won't let me critique papers. They know I can. But people don't hire me. They don't want to pay me. But they like me and know I can write. This is a business decision. Maybe I'm wrong. But I'm sorry," I said.

"You're using an analogy, comparing me to literary agents. I see. But I still want a reason why you're firing me," Jim answered.

"We're two very different people. I don't complain. I'm very independent. I only listen to Amanda, Dan, and creative people. Not you! I have a writing career. I need to write each day. I can't wait for you. I'm sorry. It's a business decision."

Mom appeared outside of the bedroom's door, staring at Jim who looked ready to yell.

"So, it's a business decision," Jim said.

"Yeah, I'm sorry," I told him.

"Well, I disagree. I'm a great care attendant, unlike some other care attendants who steal or exert physical force and/or sexual abuse their clients. You're just starting to get into the system. I need this job to keep my health-care insurance for my chronic back pain. Please give me another chance," Jim pleaded.

I gave Mom a hard stare. My mouth was parched. Sweat dripped from my armpits, back, and forehead. I wanted the moment to end. It felt like I was taking a final exam that never ended.

"I'm sorry, but it's over," I said.

Coal walked into the room.

"Hi, Coal," said Jim. He tried to pet Coal, but Coal walked out of the room and switched his tail at him.

Lou worked six days a week after Jim left, but only for four weeks until he had his accident.

A month passed without a care attendant. Mom resumed her morning care duties for me.

I didn't have to wonder when or if my attendant might arrive. Life remained the same.

It's a New Life! Mom is Gone

The Long-term Living Coalition human-resources scheduler looked for a replacement, but finding a person willing to work on the outskirts of Madison for ten dollars an hour, caring for a physically disabled person for three hours a day, was hard to find. The scheduler did find a female care attendant who watched Mom give me a sponge bath in bed, but after Mom informed the attendant that she needed to use the hoyer lift to transfer me, the attendant didn't think that she could due to her bad back. The scheduler found another female care attendant a week later named Rea.

Her physical strength and stout body gave Rea the ability to run the hoyer. She lifted and turned me with ease.

I didn't know if I wanted to have a woman washing my penis and assisting me in using the urinal. I knew that I needed to get over my modesty. It didn't help that I worried about the small size of my member. On Rea's first day, I didn't urinate because I needed to know more about her to gain her trust

She fed me lunch. Rea sat at the dining room table talking as Mom and I listened.

"My family is from the South side of Chicago. I live in Leeds an hour away from Madison. We live in Leeds because housing is cheaper. Rent is so darn expensive in Madison, but I want to live here since my mother and sister live in Sun Prairie. But my stupid husband says no to living closer to Madison. He's a trucker so I'm home a lot! I hate being alone! And I hate the Fourth of July!" Rea said.

"Why?" asked Mom.

"A couple of years ago, my seven-year-old boy drowned in a swimming pool on the Fourth of July. It's been hard. My husband and I are trying to conceive, but nothing has happened," Rea told us.

She took off the next weekend since it happened to be the Fourth of July. When Rea first sponge-bathed me alone, I became sexually aroused.

I watched her wash my erect penis with a soapy washrag. It made me became excited and I ejaculated when she rolled me over on my stomach. I felt embarrassed, making me worried that she might tell Mom, but she just cleaned the pool of semen with a damp rag.

Rea yelled at Mary, "I need a washcloth." When she arrived the next morning, Rea ran into the bathroom. Violent vomit heaves echoed through the condominium.

Several minutes passed before Mom helped Rea to her car. Mom then dressed me and got me up.

Rea took off a couple of days, but she did work on Friday to have her time sheet stamped. She promised to work on Saturday morning.

I lay in bed, staring at my clock radio that read 10:57. It was almost an hour past the time she was supposed to arrive.

She didn't call to cancel. Where was she?

"Ma, I need to get up," I shouted.

"I'm coming," Mom called.

During lunch, I envisioned lying in bed all day soaked in urine as I waited for my attendant to come. I read a preseason football magazine. Then I decided to email Rea, checking on her, and reminded her that I expected her to always call when she missed a day.

She finally called on Sunday morning to tell Mom that she had a miscarriage, and she wouldn't be able to return for a while.

Mom and I felt sorry for her. For the next two weeks, Mom took care of me.

Rea finally showed up unannounced. She gave me a bath and fed me. Rea complained about being in pain. Rea left early and took off a couple more days. She worked the following Monday before she and her husband were in a car accident. Her husband broke both of his legs. She hurt her back, but she still needed to work. Rea worked a couple of days before she called us to claim that her mother-in-law fell down the basement stairs while caring for her husband. She never developed a bond with me.

I never urinated in front of her as I waited to pee until after she left. After the mother-in-law accident, I emailed Tara to fire Rea. Before I sent it, Mom caught me and deleted the message. I grumbled to myself.

Rea called an hour late on Friday morning to explain that there had been an emergency at her other client's house. She arrived just in time and fed me lunch. Rea talked about her morning. "I soaped her fat body when the lights went out, and then she began to cough up blood everywhere! Her mentally retarded children started to cry. I didn't know what to do! So, I wrapped her up in a towel the best I could and waited for the paramedics. Poor woman! Well, I'm off to Missouri to see my husband. He has his needs. But I'm not staying at his brother's. We're going to a hotel where we can be alone, but I'll be here on Monday."

I laughed, recalling a day earlier in the week when she talked about her husband.

"His brother came from Missouri to take him back home. Good riddance, I say! He drove me nuts always ringing a bell whenever he wanted something. His mother spoiled him, making homemade dishes like collard greens, hogshead, and sweet-potato pie. He has been eating like a horse. It's disgusting, let me tell you. I won't miss him one bit! Men are pigs!" Rea exclaimed.

I knew that Rea wouldn't be back on Monday. When the phone rang around nine on Monday, I just turned over, falling back to sleep. After I ate, I asked Mom, "Can I fire her?"

"Yes," Mom said.

I wrote a long elaborate email to Tara, detailing Rea's absences and a lack of work ethic. My unbiased point of view prompted Long-term Living Coalition to fire her. It frustrated me that some people seemed to not care about having a job. I fought and looked for work to do. Being employed was a privilege, not a right. Some people always found an excuse for not hiring me. In fact, I even considered giving up my part-time Forensics teaching position since I didn't know when or if Rea would show up.

The experience with Rea left Mom and me numb. We felt used. I needed to talk about it and emailed Amanda, Dan, Mac, and Lynn about my fears. I wondered what my future held with care workers like Rea.

Care attendants blew like the wind at times, taking a piece of my heart with them. I cared about my attendants, but I kept my distance to avoid being hurt. My attendants would learn that I was their boss, not Mom. My Mom greeted my caregivers at the door as she showed them inside with a smile on her face, but I expected performance from my workers. My Mom saw my attendants as friends, but they were actually my employees.

When an attendant quit or there was a problem, Mom didn't know what to do. I handled situations that came up, especially during the last years of Mom's life. It made things difficult when Mom wanted to know who was working what shift while I was simply trying to write.

I had no control after Mom passed away. A line of care workers would just show up to be trained by Ken or Rick. My privacy and modesty disappeared while two or three attendants watched Ken or Rick give me a bed sponge bath. I still couldn't urinate in front of two people.

Life is going to change on a dime the minute Mac leaves. I'm frightened, but I also want to be independent. Welcome to adulthood, Steven! I email Larry Watson, telling him about Mom and asking if I can do this.

His reply addresses that question.

If anyone else asked me that, I would be uncertain. But given your track of accomplishment, you absolutely can. Take good care, Larry

My mentor and college classmates all believe I can live on my own. I love challenges! The biggest challenge of my life has just fallen into my lap. My career is ready to take off! It's on me now! I will be calling the shots from now on.

I read the last pages of a chapter as I get ready to begin another writing session. It's about time for me to go to work, but Mac is on the computer. I watch him. I know what he is going to say.

Mac stretches his arms high in the air. He tilts the chair all the way back on its rear legs, yawning and staring at the computer screen. Mac looks at me and shouts, "The Brewers beat the Giants 1 to 2 last night in the bottom of the ninth on a Ryan Braun home run on the last out with the count three to two. It was tied. His ERA is 400 with twenty-two homers. Well, writer you're living with me, and we'll take the cats."

"I can't live with you. We'll kill each other. No way! Impossible," I say.

I always wanted to live in Beaver River with Amanda and Dan. The system doesn't give much choice to the disabled.

It's a New Life! Mom is Gone

The State allocated most of its funds for assisted living for the populated counties like Milwaukee, Dane, Brown, and Racine counties, where the vast majority of disabled people live in urban areas. Rural and less-populated counties received a small sum each year to fund long-term assisted care for the disabled. People with disabilities living in rural counties were put on waiting lists. The waiting lists for assisted care in rural counties might take up to twenty years to receive assisted care for a physically disabled person. Mom applied for services in Colombia County when Mom and I lived in Poynette. I was ninety-seven on the waiting list. Three years later, I'd only jumped to ninety-three. My social worker wanted to put me in a foster home and have me work in a rundown community workshop with developmentally disabled people to build pallets. She suggested to Mom that we move to Madison. Another problem was my Social Security was too high according to my system. All of my life I was told that I couldn't work. Later I would learn that I needed to be employed in order to have several thousand dollars in my checking account. If I didn't work, I just could only have five-hundred dollars in my savings. In fact, I couldn't make over nine-hundred dollars a year. I made three-hundred dollars to critique papers for Stan, the speech instructor at the technical college. It's just another stupid rule, in my opinion, to employ the cognitively disabled in community workshops, to pay the developmentally disabled some money to do mundane tasks. It showed that the disabled were employed and a part of society. If I ever did receive an advance to publish a book or had a best-seller, I would have to put the money in a Special Needs trust fund in order to receive care. I couldn't make money or live where I wanted. If I moved to Beaver River, I forfeited my eligibility to receive home health care. Then I would be put on another waiting list to become eligible to receive care in Beaver River. It wasn't an option. I felt defeated.

Steven B. Salmon

Chapter Eleven

SUICIDE IS NOT AN OPTION

The cold reality strikes me at that moment. I will be living on my own in only a short matter of time. My emotions swing up and down. When I look at Amanda, standing near me, I'm having a rough time when I say, "I can't do this! I'll kill myself. I'll die."

"Knock it off. How dare you say that to us, especially after what happened to your friend, Frank, who committed suicide? You promised us. I'm ashamed of you," Amanda says.

"You're right. Amanda, I'm sorry. Dying isn't the answer. My book is being marketed to publishers in New York. Maybe someday, Amanda, it will happen. I can't give up now. Amanda, I love you! You always make me think. How do you that?" I ask.

"Because I know you like a book, and we need you! Don't you ever forget the feelings that you had about what he did. Never do that to us. Promise?" Amanda says, looking me in the eye.

"I won't. I promise you," I say.

I remembered my friend's funeral in vivid detail. After I had received an email from an acquaintance of Frank's, saying that he had passed away, I stared at the email for several minutes in disbelief. Frank was dead. It couldn't be true. How did it happen? There had to be a mistake. I sent out an email to my friends and family to tell them of my friend's death. The first reply came from Amanda a few minutes later. The email read:

I'm so sorry, Steven, to hear about your friend. What happened? Is there anything that I can do? Amanda

Emails from my friends kept pouring into my inbox throughout the afternoon with condolences, but I kept sending out queries to agents and publishers for my third book. I needed to keep moving forward. At the end of the afternoon, I had received another email from Frank's acquaintance with an invitation to attend the funeral and directions to the church. I spent the weekend debating whether or not to go. There were papers to critique for

Stan, and I needed to finish writing a long post for my blog. But during the Packers/Cowboys game on Sunday Night Football I heard my inner writer's voice. The voice said, "You need to go. Please come. I need you. Please come."

It grew louder and louder through the night, keeping me awake. I thought that I might have heard my friend's voice telling me to come. Then I decided to go to the funeral. My care attendant dressed me and put me in my electric wheelchair. I ate very little for lunch to avoid having an accident.

My Mom and I arrived at the church on time. After I drove the electric wheelchair inside, I headed to the open doors of the auditorium, filled with tearful mourners. People in wheelchairs sat in the aisles. Pretty women lined the seats.

Frank loved women. He often would ask women out on dates just by driving up to them in his electric wheelchair. Frank flashed his famous smile at women and glanced into their eyes with his deep baby-blue eyes that somehow communicated that he wanted a date. He usually came away with an email address and a date. Frank always managed to find gorgeous women to ask out. He wanted to have a physical relationship with a woman, but Frank never found a woman willing to have sex. Frank frequented whorehouses and strip clubs. He watched strippers ride the pole and dance naked in front of him. Frank stared at breasts and vaginas while ejaculating in his pants. He once drove his power chair into a car while coming out of a strip joint. Frank paid to see peep shows. He watched hookers pretend to give him a blow job through the glass window

At his funeral, I saw my friend's mother as she knelt beside the white coffin. Then I heard her anguished voice, "Look at all of these people here just for you. You go do this to us. How dare you! Why? Why? Just look at the people here for you. Why, Frank? Why? We need you! We love you! Why, God? Why?"

She collapsed on the floor. Her family members gathered her up into their arms. Relatives helped her walk out of the auditorium as she staggered up the aisle, clinging to a wad of tissues in her hands. The family disappeared for a long time.

An eerie silence filled the church after she left. The only sounds were the muffled cries and coughs from mourners. I wondered what the hell was going on. The family finally reappeared and took their seats in front of the casket.

It's a New Life! Mom is Gone

A young man who was the stepbrother of Frank stood up. He grabbed a microphone. Then he started to speak. He paced back and forth as he talked to the mourners, "Thank you for coming today. We don't know why Frank drove his wheelchair off of Monona Terrace into Lake Mendota. But we know that he was loved by all. It doesn't seem real that he is…"

The young man named Bill broke down. Now suicidal thoughts rang in my head. I knew I had Frank's courage, but the act itself struck me hard. The song, "Lean on Me" was played at his funeral. Tears formed in my eyes when I heard that song; it made me think about my friends, but their voices also told me, "It's time to be a writer." My rigid muscles became tighter when I started to make mental notes in my mind of the funeral. What made an indelible impression with me was the pain and anguish that Frank caused to his loved ones. Earlier in the fall, I had emailed Amanda, saying that I was thinking of committing suicide. I had queried my suspense manuscript to agents all summer long, getting rejected, and started writing a new manuscript. In my mind, I knew that without an agent that all of my hard work didn't matter to the news media. Knowing the likelihood of being ignored by the media made me feel like a complete failure. But now I wanted to live.

My friend's acquaintance came up to me after the service and said, "You're the author. I'm pleased to finally meet you. I wished that we had met under better circumstances. Frank talked about you often. He wanted to walk."

"Do you want to walk?" the acquaintance asked.

"No. I'm just a writer," I said. I often forgot that I was an author. In the back of my mind I knew people were reading what I was writing after my article appeared in a Milwaukee newspaper, attacking Governor Walker's long-term health care. There wasn't much recognition being an author except getting interviewed by a reporter, but it still was a rare event. When people called me an author it lacked significance in my mind, quickly vanishing from my thoughts.

I wanted to return home to see Ashes and Coal Frank taking his own life made me angry, considering he drove his electric wheelchair everywhere in Madison and owned his own house. To others it appeared that Frank always had a smile on his face, driving down State Street in his power chair, "bumping" into pretty women, and having people stop him to say hello—from my perspective the night of the funeral while I watched Monday Night Football with Coal, who kept me company in the tattered recliner. It seemed that Frank had committed a selfish act. I watched reruns of *Cheers*, thinking about my people, especially my college classmates. I cried listening to "Everyone Knows Your Name," until I finally fell asleep.

A horrible nightmare woke me up in the early morning hours. I dreamt that I saw a wedding party on the beautiful rooftop garden of Monona Terrace on a clear autumn morning. A light breeze blew, making the peonies and the different colored mums flutter in the decorative cement flower beds scattered around the rooftop. After the marriage ceremony had ended, the wedding party gathered on the edge against the railing, staring at the aqua grayish water, sipping Champagne from wine glasses. The party made a toast and took pictures of the couple when someone shouted, "Don't do it!" A crowd looked in the distance, and saw an electric wheelchair as it zoomed down a wooden pier. A giant splash rippled across the lake when the chair hit the water. The partygoers looked away when a zapping noise was heard, electrocuting Frank the instant the battery impacted the tranquil aqua green surface. Silence filled the atmosphere for a minute or two as a light blew, knocking off autumn leaves from maple trees and oak trees on the outer banks of Lake Mendota. Then the electric wheelchair sunk to the bottom of the lake.

I needed my people. The next afternoon I emailed my friends and family. The email read:

People,
I promise to never commit suicide. It's awful! I want to live now. I love you. Steven

Amanda replied first. Her email read:

Thank you for the promise. Amanda

I would hear, read and remind myself over and over again that I have a lot to live for, especially when life becomes overwhelming with disappointments and difficulties. My fortitude will be tested!

Chapter Twelve

I CAN DO THIS

Lynn promises to visit more. She returns to Milwaukee when Tara, Becky, and Flo leave. Lynn has a project deadline for her job that she has to meet in a week. She has the girls to take care of, but now she has a big mess to sort through that Mom had created. Lynn and I will see each other in the next few weeks while we work out problems with the estate and my Special Needs trust fund. My sister is back in my life.

Mac is back on my computer as he checks his email. He is getting ready to leave for Minnesota, but fiddling around with my computer like he always does.

Amanda is feeding me barbecued potato chips at the dining room table.

My attendant, Ken, has gone to the grocery store to pick up some food for me before my new care attendants take over. Karo is coming at one when Ken's three-hour shift ends. I want to say goodbye to Mac without my care workers around.

I keep an eye on my computer. "Don't goof up my computer or I'll kill you!" I say in a loud voice.

"You don't do anything anyway. All you do is write about nothing! Anyone can write," Mac says.

"Fuck you! I write every day! I'm an author with three books!" I say.

"Calm down, Steven!" Amanda shouts.

Amanda drops a potato chip on the floor. Ashes appears out of nowhere and starts licking the barbecue sauce off of the chip. He loves the taste of barbecue potato chips the best, along with sour cream chips. I watch the cat lick the potato chip, trying to ignore my cousin, snickering.

Mac stretches in the chair as he hops off it to go to the bathroom. Then he begins to sing in the bathroom.

"Is he so annoying all of the time?" Amanda asks.

"Yes. He means well, but he's so hyper. He'll drive anyone cuckoo in a short time. I love him. But I can't live with him. I need my space and quiet to write. He's taking a dump now," I say.

I have a fond memory of Mac when we were teenagers. I was sitting in my electric wheelchair outside, under an apple tree while I waited for Mac. I was stuck in the mud, but he was in the house, sitting on the toilet for an hour. I yelled "Gravel" until I was hoarse, but he always took forever in the bathroom!

When I was with Mac anywhere, he always made a pit stop, making me wait. I asked Mac why he always took a dump before going somewhere and he didn't know why.

"I didn't need to know that!" Amanda exclaims.

The phone rings. Amanda answers it.

Mac comes out of the bathroom. He stares at me and asks, "Are you sure that you don't want to live with me?"

"No," I say.

"You're a stubborn jackass! Well, I have to roll the bowl to get my ass in gear. I have to be at work at six. I suppose that I should be going," Mac says.

He sits back down in the chair again playing with the mouse. Mac pretends to play his electric guitar, letting out a loud sheik, making Ashes run to hide. Mac yawns and raises his voice again, saying, "I should be on the road by now. My work sucks! But I have to check out ESPN.com. I have to check how my fantasy-football picks are doing and staying current. You need to stay current!"

Mac stares at me, saying, "We should have put you in assisted living a long time ago. You know, Author. But you're so stubborn with your bad ugly habits, not letting anyone clean you up but your Mom and Dad. I can take care of you, but you won't let me. I want to help, you know."

Tears are already rolling down my cousin's cheeks. "I love you, Gravel. But it wouldn't work out. We're two very different people. You know that. I'll be okay." I start to cry.

"But how will you manage?" Mac asks.

"I don't know yet. But I will," I say.

He shrugs his shoulders. Mac grabs his red duffel bag from the floor. He puts the bag on his lap before he zips it. Mac sighs and yawns again. He stretches, rubbing his enormous beer belly with his hands. Mac yells, "I need to get my butt going! I have some editing to do back at the station for the ten o'clock news. Its sucks! Well, I suppose I have to go."

"Will you be okay?" Mac asks me.

"Yeah," I say.

"Are you sure?" Mac asks.

"Yes! I have Amanda. Go!" I say.

He stands up, holding the duffel bag in his hands as he begins to walk to the door. Mac leans against the wall, swaying the bag back and forth. "Email me if you need anything and I'll come."

"I will. Go! Please visit more," I say.

"I promise!" Mac says.

"I love you, Gravel."

"Goodbye," Mac says.

I start to cry the minute I hear the door open and close.

Amanda walks out of the kitchen and into the dining room. She sees me crying and asks, "Is he gone?"

"Yeah," I say.

"Are you okay?" Amanda asks.

"No. I'm afraid that I'll be alone."

"You'll never be alone and you know that. Your friends in Madison will take you out. Dan and I will visit more than we have. We promise that we will," Amanda says.

"But everybody will forget me. I'll be alone."

"Quit feeling sorry for yourself. I recall reading a post from your blog that read: 'My friends are an email away. When I need them, I just email them.' Those are your words that you recently wrote," Amanda replies.

I laugh. In an instant, Coal jumps up on the table. The table shakes when Coal leaps up in front of me. He meows and then stares at me before lying down in front of me.

I pet Coal for a while trying to be careful not to be too rough with my gross hand movements. For several minutes, I run my right balled fist across Coal saying, "I love you, Coal."

Ken pushes his bicycle inside the condominium as he carries a bag of groceries, and Karo follows him. "I got you what wanted—steak, French bread, pizza and ice cream." Ken says, taking the food in the kitchen.

"Thank you, Ken."

"Hi, Steven, how are you?" Karo asks, breaking into a big smile and laughing.

"Okay. I want to write," I say to Karo.

"What?" Karo asks.

"I will write, please," I say.

"Huh?" Karo asks, with a puzzled expression on her face.

I begin to slowly pronounce the three words again when Ken comes over and says, "Steven wants to write. I'll show you."

"Oh, I'm so sorry," Karo says.

Ken takes me to my desk. After he locks my brakes, Ken shows Karo how to place the head array in the back of the wheelchair. Then he tightens it, twisting a knob tight to prevent the head array from wiggling.

Karo is watching Ken's every move. Then I operate the computer.

"I'll be back tonight," Ken tells me before hopping on his bike.

"Okay, Ken. Thank you," I say.

I begin to write when Amanda appears in the hallway as she carries a box of books and says, "I'll take these romance novels of your mom's to the used bookstore." Mom read countless romance books that clutter the living room and her bedroom.

"Okay," I tell her

"I'll be back," Amanda says, somehow managing to negotiate the big box through the door.

I am finally alone, writing in utter silence as I enjoy the peace for a couple of minutes until Karo sweeps the den and disturbs me. People have swept the floor numerous times in the last four days after Mom passed away. I don't see why the floor has to be so clean. All that I want is to be alone, but I can't since someone always has to be with me now.

The semi-silence gives me time to write a massive email to my family and family that reads:

People,
Mom was an incredible woman. Life is sure going to be different without her. I can do this. And I will! It won't be easy, but Beaver River says that I can do anything now. Our book is in New York. Please don't come all at

*once. Please get together to plan your visits. I will need
you! I love you. I will be in touch. Steven*

I email a blog posting to my friend, Cory, who publishes
them on my blog for me. The posting reads:

*Life keeps changing. But it is the ability to adjust that is
the key to life.*

For the next ten minutes, I delete countless enticing
emails from my publisher, asking for more money to pay for book
reviews and newspaper articles in major national newspapers. It
makes me mad that I even had to pay for e-books and spend more
money in order to have my books shown at book fairs around the
world. What author didn't want that kind of recognition for their
book? I had to pay to have an agent represent my books, or have
an e-book agent represent my e-books. Also, my publisher wanted
me to pay for a book tour and to buy foreign rights. I had to
purchase my books at an outrageous author's "discount" from my
publisher to carry my books in local bookstores on consignment.
Some local bookstores refused to carry my books or have a book
signing. My publisher had a nonrefundable book policy, which
made local bookstore managers not want to sell my books. The
major bookstores like Barnes & Noble didn't carry my publisher's
overpriced paperback books. I used what little money that I earned
from critiquing speech outlines from Stan to buy books and e-
books. My case manager tried to help me find an organization
willing to finance my writing career but no disabled groups
wanted to help an aspiring author with Cerebral palsy. I kept
pursuing my dream. The barriers that I faced made me feel very
small and insignificant at times.

Karo mops, making more noise. She asks me, "Hey,
Steven. What do you want to eat?"

I answer, "Pizza, please."

"You want pizza," Karo replies, repeating the same words
to make sure that she understands what I want.

"Yeah," I say

She walks in the kitchen to fix the pizza.

It seems strange to me that Karo is preparing my pizza at
two in the afternoon. I just keep emailing people and blogging.

When I see Karo sit at the dining room table, watching her talk on her phone, I continue to write. Then I feel fluid excrement running down my legs. I stink like rotten eggs! It embarrasses me, but I haven't had a bowel movement for three days. Diarrhea falls onto the floor.

Amanda returns, but Karo sees the poop and says, "Oh, oh, Steven. You've a mess. I'll clean you up."

I don't say anything.

Amanda says, "It's okay, Steven. There's nothing to be ashamed about."

Karo takes off the head array before pushing me into my bedroom. She uses the hoyer lift to transfer me from my manual wheelchair to the bed but not before she puts a terrycloth towel on the mattress. She releases the straps from the hoyer after lowering me on the bed and backs the hoyer away. Karo take off my shoes and socks. She then wrestles the soggy, soiled blue jeans from my extra tight legs. After tossing the dirty pants in a laundry basket, Karo removes my Depends, dumping it in a white plastic trashcan. She moves the can near the bed and starts using baby wipes to clean me up. Karo uses a half can of wipes to clean the mess. She changes her gloves before putting on a new pair of Depends on me. Karo grabs a fresh pair of jeans from my closet. She struggles to pull up the pants on my lower torso. She scoots the green sling under me by rolling me on my side. Karo brings the hoyer back. She puts the straps on the black iron bars, and she puts on my socks and shoes. She then lifts me up as she transfers me to the manual wheelchair. She undoes the straps, pushes the hoyer out of the way, tugs the sling from under me, and repositions me in the seat before buckling my seat belt.

"I go pee, Karo," I tell her.

Karo retrieves the urinal from the bathroom's cabinet. She opens my fly, pulls down my Depends, and aims my penis inside the urinal before I urinate. Karo empties and rinses the urinal. She returns me to the living room.

Karo pushes me in front of the television. She heads into the bathroom to retrieve two tablets of Imodium from the medicine cabinet. Karo gives me the medication with some iced tea back at the dining room table. She feeds me the pizza. While Karo gives me my supper, I take another "dump" in my pants.

I don't eat a lot since I feel uncomfortable when I ask for a lemon drop to suck on.

"I want to watch TV, Karo."

"Okay, Steven." Karo says, pushing me back to the TV to give me time to digest my food. She starts to clean the table.

I fall asleep for a few minutes. The Baclofen makes me sleepy. Sleep becomes precious to me. But I can't sleep. Work is becoming too much to do. There are emails to answer and write. Becky and Flo are in contact with me. After I wake up, I say, "Karo, I want to write, please."

"Steven, can you wait? I'm doing the dishes," Karo calls from the kitchen.

I don't like having to wait, but I need a break. I relax for a couple more minutes until Karo pushes me to my desk.

She sets me up at the computer and puts in the head array on back of the wheelchair. I tap the head array to make the inbox appear allowing me to go back to work.

"Are you okay?" Karo asks me.

"I'm okay," I tell her, going in my writer's zone.

Karo goes to my bedroom to change the bed and clean my room.

I'm in my element, writing alone when Amanda opens the door. My entire body jumps when Amanda appears.

Amanda looks at me and says, "We need to talk, Steven. I received a text from John, saying that Hannah broke her leg. My daughter needs me. I have a cab coming in five minutes to take me to Badger Bus. I'm sorry, Steven."

It shocks me, realizing that I will be on my own now, but I tell Amanda that I understand.

"You know that you can do this," Amanda reassures me.

"I know but it won't be easy," I say.

"You can do anything now, remember," Amanda says, looking at her wristwatch.

"I'm coming to Beaver River," I tell her.

"Well, come! And remember that your friends and family are just an email away. I have to go. Bye, author. Email me," Amanda says, walking out the door.

I nod in her direction. Tears fill my eyes when I hear the door close, but I keep tapping Morse code, moving forward.

Steven B. Salmon

Chapter Thirteen

MOM IS GONE

My mind is in a daze as I ride the bus to the doctor's office. I need to increase my Baclofen dosage since my muscles are getting tighter. I'm running errands now on my own, including one to get new armrests for my manual wheelchair. Since the armrests fell off the chair, I've had to rest my elbows on the iron bars. I think about Mom on these rides, feeling lost, scared, tired, and independent. I'm doing what Dan and Amanda expect, which is to make it in the world. "I can do this," I tell myself countless times.

Everything seems strange to me as I'm now out of the house on a regular basis. Neighbors come up to me when I'm outside waiting for the bus and say, "Steven, I'm sorry for your loss. I hear that you're an author. Where can I buy your books?"

"My books are at the University Bookstore," I say, but they don't understand me. It's frustrating. Here is my opportunity to sell books after all these years when Mom refused to hand out my business card to people. It doesn't matter now since the books are out of print. It feels good to get recognition for my books, but soon the bus arrives and the neighbor says, "Well, Steven, it's good to see you outside. If there's anything that I can do, just let me know."

"Okay, thank you," I say, driving onto the lift to be whisked away by the bus.

Flo meets me at the doctor's office and the wheelchair store. She always has a smile on her face and kind words to say like, "Steven, Honey. How's it going?"

"It's going. Your author needs food. I can't write without something to eat," I tell her.

"I'll bring some groceries over. What do you like to eat?" Flo asks.

"I want steak, French bread, watermelon, and chocolate ice cream," I reply.

"You got it. Tomorrow, I have two houses for you to look at and one more on Wednesday."

"Okay," I say, yawning.

After the doctor's appointment, I return to the condominium where Karo greets me, "Hi, I want to write," I tell her.

She transfers me from the electric wheelchair to the manual wheelchair, using the hoyer. Then she sets me up at the computer to work. "What do you want to eat?" Karo asks.

"I want ham, potatoes, peas, and ice cream. Thank you, Karo."

"You want potatoes and ice cream, right?" Karo asks me.

"Yes, but I want ham and peas, too," I say.

"Oh, you want to go to pee," Karo says.

"No, I want p-e-a-s and h-a-m;" I say the words slowly spelling out "peas" and "ham," hoping that Karo understands me on the first try.

"You want peas and ham." Karo answers.

"Yes, Karo," I exclaim, though I realize I have to play spelling games with all of my care attendants from time to time

"I'm so sorry, Steven," Karo replies.

"That's okay, Karo," I tell her. Then I start to write emails as Karo goes into the kitchen to fix my supper. My day has just started. It's a new life. I email friends and family a massive email to tell them about looking at houses. The email reads:

People,
Tomorrow, I will go look at houses to live. I guess that I can do this. I will keep you posted. Steven

After I send the message, I write a posting to Cory to publish on my blog. Karo interrupts me, saying, "Eh, Steven. There's no ham."

I'm mad, but I say, "I want pizza and salad."

"You want pizza, right?" Karo says.

"Yes," I say, getting back to my writing.

The posting read:

Cory,
Please post. Thank you. Steven

My mind is spinning in circles like a stripper, twisting on the pole. Days are continuous now. There are no breaks anymore. Just decisions to make! Last week Mom went to McDonald's and she asked what I wanted to eat. That was the only decision that I had to make. Now I'm choosing the house that I want to live in rather than picking if I want a cheeseburger or a Big Mac. Now I can make any decision that I want. It's just weird.

I hear a couple of dings while I'm writing the posting. My mind knows that it's Cathy and Amanda, offering words of wisdom to me. The large network of friends has become my support system. After I do the code for Alt and S, the email is sent. I read Cathy's and Dan's emails by using the Up Arrow to open the messages to read. Dan's email reads:

Way to go! You can do it! Dan

Then I move down a line to highlight the next line. Cathy's message reads:

How exciting! Take one step at a time. Cathy

I look over at the dining room table to see pizza, a mug of iced tea, and my Baclofen waiting for me. Then I turn to glance at the clock above the tattered recliner where Coal sleeps in a big ball. The time is 3:35. It's too early. I'm not ready to eat. Usually I have supper at a quarter to five. I want a salad with that pizza, but Amanda always tells me to roll with it. After I hide the Co:Writer word predication window, I smile at Karo when she says in an African-American accent, "Pizza."

"Yeah, pizza. I want to go pee," I tell her.

"Eh, what, you want to go pee?" Karo asks.

"Yeah, I want to pee." I smile at Karo as I continue to tap Morse code.

"Okay," Karo says, taking the head array off the back of the manual wheelchair. She starts to push me to my bedroom to take me the bathroom.

"I go pee here, Karo," I say.

"Okay," Karo says, retrieving the urinal from my bathroom. She assists me in using the urinal. Karo empties the urinal in the bathroom before she puts me back together. Then she pushes me to the table to eat, sitting down in a captain chair to feed me. Karo picks up the mug and places the straw near my mouth, but I say, "No, Karo. I want my pill."

"Oh, sorry, Steven," Karo says, putting the mug back on the table and placing the tablet in my mouth. Then she grabs the mug and puts the straw in between my lips. Karo wipes my mouth with a towel before giving me the pizza.

I eat the pizza in silence as I enjoy my pepperoni pizza with garlic crust with mushrooms, but it lacks the extra cheese that Mom used to always put on. It's my pizza! I have three pieces, being careful not to overeat since I already have an upset stomach. Then I jump when the door opens and Lynn appears, holding a pot in her hands. She says, "Steven, this is Mom. Do you want Mom in your room or her room?"

For a moment, I don't know to say. It hits me that Mom is gone! I say in a soft voice, "Mom's room."

Lynn has tears rolling down her cheeks as she puts the urn with Mom's ashes on a bookshelf in Mom's bedroom.

Karo gives me the rest of my tea which I gulp down in a few seconds.

When I finish drinking, I say, "Candy, Karo, please." I begin to cough and gag.

Lynn says, "He needs candy now." She takes a peppermint from my backpack and places it in my mouth.

"Oh, oh, I forgot about giving Steven the candy; sorry," Karo tells Lynn.

"He needs candy after he eats or Steven will throw up his entire meal," Lynn tells Karo. "Now, Steven, I want you to write a poem for Mom's memorial service."

"Okay, I'll write it tonight," I say.

"Also, I told you to not email your lawyer without ccing me. Then you gave her a wrong date to meet you to set up your will and trust. You have to listen to me!" Lynn yells.

"I'm sorry. I'm tired!" I say, yawning. I haven't slept much since Mom's passing.

"Every email that you send your lawyer costs you money. If you want to waste your money, that's up to you! I'm done,"

Lynn exclaims, slamming the door and leaving the condominium without saying goodbye

I feel that I have lost my sister again! No matter what I say or do, it's wrong. My sister isn't like Amanda, who I can tell anything to. The difficult part of my sister is her sensitive side. Lynn tends to hold a grudge against a person for a very long time.

I just don't know what to do about Lynn. I take a deep sigh before saying, "I want to write, please."

"Okay," Karo says, pushing me over to my desk and putting the head array on the back of the wheelchair.

Then I go back to checking my email before entering into Word to create a document to write Mom's poem. There are no new emails in my inbox, but I shoot an email to my lawyer anyway to change the date of our meeting and apologize for my mistake. I exit Outlook Express to move My Documents to create a new document. Then I start writing the poem while Karo watches a movie from her tablet on the sofa. It's finally quiet for me to write. I'm in my zone.

Mom

We are here today
to celebrate the life of Mary M. Salmon.

Take a look around at the rolling terrain
The contoured fields of corn and hay
with gravel roads,
dotting the beautiful landscape
The scent of cow dung hangs in the air

This is definitely Wisconsin!

Mom never wanted anything or complained.
All that she wanted was
for Lynn and me to be happy

Mom believed in the impossible dream.
Against the odds, she created an
Author with years of sacrifice.

It's hard living with an author
With the disappointments,
rejections and deadlines to meet.
And the daily grind of writing—

She just smiled at me.
Thank you, Mom, for everything
I will make you proud.

Steven

"Karo, come here."

"Coming, Steven," Karo says, walking over to the computer.

"Please read it," I say, pointing at the computer screen.

Karo slowly reads the poem aloud in her broken English as I smile at her. When Karo finishes reading the poem, she says, "That's good, Steven."

I lean my head on her shoulder and fall asleep.

Chapter Fourteen

HOUSE HUNTING

I don't wake up until six in the morning when the intercom buzzes, signaling the beginning of the AM shift. An attendant comes to relieve the overnight shift. There is nothing for the attendant to do except talk on his cell phone and disturb my sleep, but I will have a care worker with me all of the time from now on. I go back to sleep. The only time that I sleep throughout the night is the night after the writer's conference in April ends. Normally I'm awake during the night as I think about what to write and what I need to do. In one of my favorite dreams I am helping to "teach" classes at Northland High School in Beaver River. I start an argument with Amanda about how to critique a purpose sentence in the introduction of a persuasive paper on purpose.

"That purpose sentence is weak, Amanda. It doesn't grab the reader's attention," I say in the dream, trying hard not to laugh.

She reads the purpose sentence several times before saying, "It's perfect. What do you mean?"

I see Dan standing in his classroom door, watching me rile her up. A moment later, I wink at him and say in a loud voice, "I disagree. It isn't developed enough."

"You need to remember that these are sophomore English papers and the students are just learning how to write," Amanda tells me.

"I know, but I still disagree," I say.

"Stop being stupid and follow my directions," Amanda replied.

"But I'm the author. I think that I know what I'm doing!" I said, starting to laugh.

"But I'm the English teacher, and you'll do it my way or else," Amanda says, hitting me in a friendly manner on the shoulder.

"Ouch, that hurts! I'm delicate," I say, mockingly laughing.

Dan laughs, too

Amanda shakes her fists at us. Her husband, Ben, who is the vice principal of the high school, is walking by the English Center and overhears the disturbance.

When he sees us shouting and laughing, Ben knows what has happened. He looks at us, saying, "All right, what's going on, as if I don't know already?"

"I'm just showing her how to critique papers. I wasn't doing anything wrong, and she goes crazy on me! I never start anything with her, you know!" I say, beaming my smile at Ben.

"You silly English people! I have to be a referee blowing my whistle, breaking up your sophomoric arguments!" Ben says, walking out of the English Center

My dream ends when I hear sweeping outside of my bedroom door. I want to yell but I don't, remembering I need to go with the flow. It occurs to me that I can do anything now! I decide right there that I'm going to Beaver River in the fall. It's time to have dreams come true. I stare at the wall with tears in my eyes and say, "I'm coming Beaver River. I'm coming!" Then I fall back to sleep until Ken knocks on my door.

Ken takes a towel that's hanging on the hoyer lift and folds it in half

"Hi, guys," I say to the cats. "How are the guys? Did you eat?"

"I'm okay. I miss you. I love you," I say.

The cats purr away while Ken takes out a pair of blue jeans and my shoes from the closet and puts them on the bed. Ken grabs a pair of socks and underwear from a dresser drawer as he puts the articles of clothing together. Next, he takes out a Packer shirt from the second drawer, putting it on the back of the wheelchair. Ken walks back to the dresser drawer for a pair of rubber gloves that he puts on his hands. He pulls down my blankets. Ken changes his gloves periodically during the process of bathing and getting me out of bed. He then maneuvers the undershirt up to my shoulders before pulling the shirt off my arms and over my head. He dampens the washcloth before lathering it with soap. Ken washes my back. He rinses me off and dries me off with a blue towel. He pulls the sweatpants halfway down while Ken checks my rectum for bits of excrement.

I pass gas throughout the night, leaving chunks of poop that need to be removed in the morning. Usually Ken needs to retrieve another warm washcloth from the bathroom to clean my rectum, but he doesn't have to this morning, thanks to the Imodium.

He removes the bottoms, taking them along with the undershirt to the dirty hamper in the walk-in closet. He returns to wash my buttocks and boney legs but doesn't wash my feet for an unknown reason. After drying me off, Ken turns me over on my stomach to wash my arms, armpits, belly, and penis. He dries my upper torso before turning me over again. Ken applies ointment to my right buttock cheek. He puts on my Depends and socks. He wrestles the blue jeans over my tight knees, skillfully tugging my pants up to my hips. Ken picks up the water basin to empty it out and puts it under the bathroom sink. He brings the urinal back, setting it on the TV stand, and removes the towel from the seat. Ashes and Coal move out of his way when he pushes the manual wheelchair up against the bedroom window. Ken locks the brakes of the wheelchair. He reaches for the green sling hanging from the hoyer and puts it beside him. He then wheels the hoyer over to the bed. Ken presses a button to lower the boom to attach the straps to the black metal hooks.

The phone rings as he raises the boom a little before he tucks my elbows in the sling. He raises the lift up more, and then maneuvers the hoyer around, positioning it in front of the manual wheelchair. Ken moves the lift closer to the wheelchair before lowering the boom down. He grabs a lobe from the sling and pulls me upright in the wheelchair as he lowers the boom. Ken unhooks the straps from the metal bars. He pushes the hoyer away with his feet without letting go of me. He manages to shift the sling from under me. Ken tosses the sling on the bed before grabbing the loops of my blue jeans from the back of the wheelchair to position me in the seat. He fastens the Velcro seat belt. He picks up the sling, putts it on the hoyer, and pushes it into the corner next to the closet and the bed.

He redoes the seat belt and my pants. Ken takes the urinal and pulls down my undergarment. After positioning the urinal, he waits for me to urinate. Ken puts me back together when I finish.

He redoes my seat belt before taking the urinal to the bathroom to empty and rinse it out.

Ken returns from the bedroom to push me to the master bathroom to brush my teeth, put deodorant underneath my arms, and wash my face. He shaves me every other day. Ken asks if I want to shave today and I reply, "No."

He takes me back to the bedroom. Ken parks the wheelchair near the bed. He reaches for the ointment that he put on his hand to apply to my dry and calloused right hand and elbow. Ken wrestles my Packers shirt over my big head and my tight arms. He sits down on the bed to put on my shoes. Ashes comes to rub against his legs, purring loudly and begging Ken to pet him. Ken pets Ashes for several minutes until he says, "That's enough, Ashes. I bet Steven is hungry."

He stands up and pushes the wheelchair through the narrow winding hallway into the dining room. Ken positions the chair a foot away from the table and locks the brakes. "What do you want to eat?"

"I want pretzels," I tell him.

Ken heads into the kitchen to fix my iced tea. He retrieves the ten milligrams of Baclofen that I take with my lunch. "Do you want cheese?"

"No," I say.

Ken sits down in a chair as he gives me a pill with the tea.

I take a deep breath after I stop drinking, sucking the straw while I watch him put on the gloves to feed me. It doesn't make me happy to see him wearing gloves when he gives me lunch. The gloves seem to give the food a rubbery flavor. But I accept that he wears gloves to avoid being bit by accident. I eat a handful of pretzels. When I finish eating, I drink the rest of the tea.

Ken wipes my mouth with a hand towel. From the glass Mason jar sitting on the counter, he retrieves a peppermint for me to suck on.

For a couple of minutes, I suck on my candy as I sit in the electric wheelchair while waiting for the bus to arrive to take me to go look at the two houses. Ken says, "I won't be able to care for you anymore since you hired Integration. "

"I know Ken. I'm sorry, but I need more care now. I don't know what else to do."

"I don't like Integration, but I understand. I guess," Ken tells me.

The intercom buzzes, making me jump.

Ken helps me to negotiate through the series of doors. Karo arrives and Ken takes her inside of the condominium as I drive to the bus. Then I maneuver the chair onto the lift and into the bus, waiting for the driver to secure the wheelchair in place.

The driver asks, "Do you have tickets?"

"Yeah, I do. The tickets are in the backpack on the wheelchair," I tell the driver, motioning my head toward the rear of the chair.

The bus driver grabs three tickets from the bag and we take off.

I'm proud of myself for being independent, but I feel strange as the bus travels across neighborhoods. It's just me now. My bus pulls up in front of a brown ranch house. I see Becky and Flo waving at me. When I get off the bus, I go up the driveway to a rickety ramp without a railing that leads into the house. I enter a small kitchen where an overweight man with thick bifocals sits and says, "Hi, I'm Eric. I'm the director for Integration. I'm sorry for your loss."

People keep saying that to me, and I always nod not knowing what to say. "Thank you. Can I have my cats and sex?" I ask them.

Eric laughs, "You don't waste time, do you? Absolutely, you can. Fred and John have female visitors come. They work during the day. So you'll have quiet time to write. I hear that you're a New York author!"

"Not yet. Maybe one day I will be," I say, starting to cry, thinking about Beaver River.

"It's okay, Steven," Becky tells me.

"Oh, Honey. Let's have a look around," Flo says, giving me a tour.

I see an open living room with a big TV, a couple of recliners, and a picture window overlooking a shady yard. Then I see the bathroom with a walk-in-shower and "my" bedroom.

After I see the house, I say, "I like it but I don't like the ramp."

"That's okay, Steven. Let's go look at the second house," Becky says.

I smile and carefully maneuver my chair down the ramp before getting on the bus.

The bus takes me to the other house within a few minutes, but I'm tired by the time the bus stops in front of a white split-level ranch house with large bay windows.

Flo ushers me inside of the enormous living room with vaulted ceilings, laminate hardwood floors and a gigantic TV. Brand-new appliances fill the fancy open kitchen. She shows me the bedrooms and then takes me outside again, down a winding cement path to the basement. When we enter the basement, I see a bar with an Everlast punching bag. Flo leads me down a hallway to an empty bedroom and says, "The man who lives in the basement is an author."

I've always wanted to live with a writer, but I see a cat. Coal and Ashes don't like other cats.

"You would have to go upstairs to eat your meals," Flo tells me.

I can't imagine going out in below-zero weather as Becky, Flo, and I head back to the living room upstairs.

Flo introduces me to a Cerebral palsy man sitting in an electric wheelchair and says, "This is Mark Winters. He is the designer of the house. Mark built it!"

"That's awesome! It's beautiful, Mark," I tell him.

"Thank you. I have read your books. You're an amazing author," Mark says.

"Thank you," I answer, believing that no one knows who I am, but everywhere I go people seem to know me. My article about Governor Walker's plan to privatize home health care has created me a name. Mom is dead, but I'm living my dream now.

When I come home, I look at my email, wishing for a message from Stasia. There is no email from her, but Amanda has emailed me. The email reads:

Steven,
How's it going? We know that you can do this but don't
get impatient. Well, Hannah and I are off to New York
to celebrate her sixteenth birthday. Be good, Steven.
Amanda

I have tears in my eyes when I tap Control and R to reply.

It's a New Life! Mom is Gone

Amanda,
Take me to New York with you. Find me an editor or a
publisher. Yes, I know that I need to be patient. Steven

New York fills my mind, making me dream, escaping the big decisions I have to make. The first house we saw is out of the question with the railing missing on the ramp. I need my cats, but I like Mark. My mind hopes that tomorrow brings an answer. I go to bed early.

The next day the bus takes me a couple of miles away from the condominium. When we pull up in front of a white ranch house, I see a power saw and sawdust in the open garage. I drive the electric wheelchair up the ramp and Flo and Becky follow me inside the house. When I enter a small kitchen, a sexy brunette introduces herself, "Hi, I'm Heather. I'm the house manager."

"Hi," I say, using my irresistible smile as I drive into an open living room. I like what I'm seeing.

"Follow me, Sweetie," Flo says, leading me down the hall to the first bedroom.

I make a big circle with my chair in the small room. Then I see a carpenter putting up tiles in the walk-in-shower. I ask Flo, "Can I have my cats here and have women over?"

"Of course, Honey," Flo tells me.

Later I ask my attendants to help me find women to have sex with, but Flo and Becky tell me that is against the rules. Clients can smoke cigarettes and weed. Why can't I have sex? I feel as if I was lied to and fall into a deep depression for several days. I think and say to my attendants that I want to kill myself, but I know that I have my people who love me. The problem is that I can't call women to arrange a meeting. I have the money to pay for a woman and a hotel room since I don't spend my spending money except to pay for lap dances at the club. My money accumulates in my checking account. My roommates use their spending money to order take-out and take the female attendants out to eat. They call any woman who enters the house their girlfriend. It embarrasses me since I want a real girlfriend. I'm so lonely. Women tell me that I'm handsome, but what woman wants a man who drools and shits in his pants? I accept not having sex.

I am allowed to masturbate in my room. I imagine being with Chris, my favorite stripper. All that I want is a book and sex.

I look at Becky and say, "I want it!"

"Okay," Becky says. "I'll take pictures of your new home and forward them to you to send to your family and friends."

"Thank you," I say, laughing, since this is my first major decision that I have made without any help. What will my family think? Beaver River believes that I can do anything. I feel great having made my decision.

Heather hugs me and says, "Welcome to the house, Hon!"

I have a big smile on my face and say, "Thank you."

After I return to the condominium Karo greets me at the door and the bus driver buzzes the intercom, letting Karo know I'm back. "Hi, Steven. How are you?" Karo asks after opening the second door of the condominium's hallway.

"I have a house, Karo," I tell her.

Karo helps me with the doors and says, "Wow! Your own house! Where is it?"

"Green Way."

"Green Way is a nice house. I will work there. Brian and Andy are nice. You'll like it!" Karo says.

I ask Karo while she transfers me from the electric wheelchair to the manual wheelchair to allow me to write, "What are Brian and Andy like?"

"Eh, they are good. You will like them, Steven."

I want to know more about my roommates, but I guess that I will find out soon enough. The transition is exciting, but scary.

"What do you want to eat, Steven?" Karo asks.

"The rest of the pizza, iced tea and ice cream, please," I tell her.

"Okay," Karo says, going to the kitchen to reheat the pizza and fix the tea.

I sit for a couple of minutes, waiting to eat my supper. Then I eat in silence as I think about what I'm going to write in the email to my friends and family. When I finish eating, I say, "I want candy and I want to write, please."

"Okay," Karo says, dropping a lemon drop in my mouth and setting me up at the computer to write. She puts the head array on the back of the manual wheelchair, leaving me alone. "Hey, Steven, I'll be in the kitchen eating. Just yell if you need me."

I nod since I'm busy loading CoWriter, opening Outlook Express and the inbox, using the mouse. The arrow can't move fast enough to click on Becky's email with pictures of what will soon be my new home. I exit Mouse Mode to tap Control and F to forward the email. Then I continue tapping my family's and friends' email addresses in the To line. I use Shift Tab to move the cursor down to the text box before using the equal keys to bring up CoWriter. Then I write the message that reads:

People,
See pictures of my house below. It's my first major
decision that I made on my own. Onward! Steven

I hide the CoWriter word prediction window. After using Alt and S, the email is sent. Then as I'm writing a new message I hear three dings that indicate I've received an email. I save the email in drafts form to look at the new message. After moving the mouse to the email, I double-click the little box next to the first reply. I get out of Mouse Mode and read three emails. The first email is from Cathy and reads.

Steven,
This is awesome. Your Mom would be proud. Take one
step at a time. Cathy

I use the Down Arrow to read the second email which is from Dan.

You can do it. Dan

The third message is from my agent, Stasia.

Dear Steven,
Congratulations! Stasia

The messages make me cry. I decide to reply to Stasia.

Stasia,

Steven B. Salmon

Is there any news on our book? Steven

I remember being at the writing conference in late March, sitting at the bar with Stasia and my friend, Bob, having a Coke, feeling like a real author, when Stasia says, "Steven, I have decided to represent all of your books." I wanted to go call Beaver River right there. I told everyone that I will soon have a book deal! My moment had finally come.

Dear Steven,
I haven't sent the book out yet. It needs more edits.
Stasia

I reply.

You lied to me. I have been telling everyone that the book is in New York. I look like a fool. I'm a failure! Maybe I will get another agent to represent me.

After sending it, I create and write a massive email to my loved ones

People,
Stasia lied. Our book isn't in New York. Mac is right. I suck. I quit. Steven

I sit there, crying. When Karo sees me she asks, "Steven, are you okay?" For several minutes, I sit in silence, staring at the wall. Dan answers my email.

Steven,
Just relax. You're too close to give it up now. Go to bed. Get some rest. Tomorrow is a new day. Dan

Chapter Fifteen

THE MOVE

The next day Ken gets me up and feeds me lunch. Soon I'm back at the computer. I don't want to be at the computer and would rather be anywhere else but at the desk. Before I start working, Flo arrives with some groceries. I'm about ready to open the inbox when Flo rubs my shoulder and says, "Hi, Hon. I have set up a time for you to meet Brian and Andy. They move in this Wednesday. After a week, then you can move in. So, I'm thinking the three of you can get together on Saturday."

"Okay," I tell her.

Then Flo says to me, "I'll set it up. Is there anything else?"

"No."

I hesitate to open the inbox, worrying that Stasia will be mad at me. When I double-click on the inbox, I see an email with a subject line that reads: Sent to nine New York publishers, including Harper Collins. Then I open the message and see the list of publishers each with positive reviews of my cover letter. The reviews read: Exciting, Thrilling, Unique, Epic and A Must Read. I'm crying when I read the email. A note from Stasia reads:

Dear Steven,
The manuscript has been sent to nine publishers in New York, including Harper Collins. You're not a failure. You're an author. Stasia

I reply:

I'm sorry that I yelled at you. There is a lot that I have to do now. Thank you. Steven

I send the email. Then I forward the message from Stasia to family and friends.
My message reads:

Steven B. Salmon

People,
New York, here I come. I'm sorry about last night. It's
an author's life. Steven

I write a post for Corey to publish on my blog. It reads:

Life goes up and down. Mom, the book is in New York.
I'm moving soon. I will keep moving forward.

I hear a ding while writing the message. After sending the email, I see that it is from Cathy.

Steven,
Take it one step at a time. Get your rest. We are here for
you but don't overdo it. Cathy

My friend, Cathy, knows me like Beaver River does. I overwork myself at times to try to prove that I can do it all. Now I have even more to do without Mom here, making sure that things are done, going places, and working on my career. Now I can stay up all night and eat whatever I want. I call my vast network of friends and family "my people." When I have something to say, good or bad, I write a massive email to them. For now I depend on my friends for support. I'm always emailing now; and friends they email me, too, checking on me.

Life has changed, but it also remains the same. My mind is in overdrive when I meet my roommates for the first time. I'm numb and very tired when I drive up the ramp to meet Brian and Andy. When Heather opens the door, she says, "Welcome, Honey."

I smile, driving my electric wheelchair into the kitchen to the dining room table where a large man, who I later learn is Brian with a mole on his right cheek, is enjoying soup. Because he is drinking from a Packers mug, I immediately like him. He smiles at me and says, "Hey Steven. How are you?"

"Okay. I love the Packers!" I exclaim.

"The Packers are my team. They play next week on Thursday," Brian tells me.

"Yeah, I can't wait for football," I say, not knowing what else to say. "I'm an author. What do you do?"

Brian shrugs. "Heather, I'm ready to go to bed," he says, yawning.

"Okay, I'll put you down," Heather tells him.

"Okay, Dear. Let's go! See you, Steven. Let's go! *The Brady Bunch* is on, Heather," Brian says, backing up the electric wheelchair and turning down the hallway to his room.

A couple of minutes later, an overweight man whose feet are missing and looks like Santa Claus enters the living room in his power chair. He doesn't say anything to me. The man heads over to his computer. He starts up his computer in the corner of the living room and begins playing Panda Pop. He stares at the computer screen until a man, wearing army fatigues, tells him, "Andy, please move your wheelchair back so I can do your blood sugar."

Andy doesn't move.

"Come on, son!" the man in fatigues exclaims, slapping Andy hard on the shoulder.

Andy yells, "Stop it, James! You're hurting me! Stop it now! I said to stop it, you motherfucker!"

Flo and Heather come to help and both say, "Calm down, Andy."

Eventually Andy relaxes and allows James to take his blood sugar.

Heather asks Andy, "What do you want to eat for breakfast?"

"I want bacon and eggs. Oh, I want six cookies." Andy laughs before saying, "I'm just kidding!"

Andy then drives over to me. He places his hand on my arm and says, "Hi, Steven. I'm a prophet. I'm praying for you to walk again in Jesus Christ's name."

Later I ask Andy and Brian what they want and they both say they want to walk. Brian asks me, "Steven, what do you want?"

"New York is what I want." I reply, dreaming and smiling.

Then Andy goes back to his computer to play Panda Pop with the game's theme music blaring.

James smiles at me and says, "Don't mind him. Welcome, my brother."

What I want Andy to pray for me about is not walking, but that I'll publish a book. In a couple of days I will live in this strange new environment, which I will call my home. For now I will go back to the condominium to enjoy my final days of quiet and peace. I don't really think about the logistics of moving nor do I have any clue what I'm getting into. Moving has always been a part of my life. I'm not scared. Part of me is thrilled to start my new life, but I'm too busy deciding what I will take with me. I take a few pieces of Mom's china to remind me of Mom along with family pictures that I want. The rest of the items after I move will go like Lynn dumps Mom's tattered recliner. Because my family is busy with their careers it's just me, Karo, Flo, and Rick who do the packing. My computer is the last thing to be packed. The last email that I write from the condominium is to Stasia. The email reads:

Stasia,
The computer will be down tomorrow. I'm moving in the afternoon. Steven

A day before I move Flo notices that Ashes hasn't eaten for several days. Karo tells Flo about Ashes. Flo and Karo sit down with me to tell me that Ashes needs to go to the vet. Then Flo takes Ashes to the vet and returns with an empty animal carrier. The vet calls a few hours later saying that Ashes has kidney failure and his teeth are bad. The veterinarian wants to insert a feeding tube into Ashes. It is not probable Ashes will survive. I don't want Ashes to suffer in pain. I decide to put Ashes to asleep. I feel guilty about having Ashes put asleep when I see Coal wander around alone. But Coal will quickly adjust to life without Ashes. It is the right decision. I email my family and friends about Ashes' death.

Amanda answers first:

Steven,
I'm so sorry. Is there anything that I can do? Amanda

It's a New Life! Mom is Gone

The pain that I feel losing Mom and Ashes overwhelms me, but I must keep moving forward. Ashes had been my cat. I took a couple of minutes, crying on Flo's shoulder, wondering how much more pain I can take. I have to stay strong. Part of me wants to give up but I can't. There are a lot of things that I still have to accomplish and that I look forward to, like getting published. My heart aches now with sorrow, but I have to make decisions, such as whether or not to take Mom's fine china. Decisions never cease. What should I keep and what should I not keep? Where do I want to put this or that? I can't grieve today.

The last email that I read before breaking down the computer is from Stan. The email reads:

Steven,
Tomorrow, life is going to change drastically. Be
prepared. Stan

The movers come to move my things. It feels like a normal move that Mom and I have made through the years, moving from one place to another, except this time Mom isn't here.

I'm supervising the move and I make sure that that I have packed everything I want. Within two hours I'm sitting in a nearly empty condominium with Karo, Coal and some useless pieces of furniture. Karo microwaves a TV dinner for me, and makes rice with peanut butter for her to eat. We eat in silence. The bus comes to make the five-minute ride to my new house. Before going outside, I enter Mom's bedroom to say goodbye. I stare at the urn that looks like a flower pot and say, "Well, Mom. Thank you for everything. It's a new life, Mom! I'll make you proud, Mom. New York, Mom!"

Karo and I sit at the end of the sidewalk as we wait for the bus. Then Karo asks, "Eh, Steven, are you going to miss your house?"

It hadn't crossed my mind up until now. "I guess," I say. For the last few years the condominium has been an isolated place where I write, eat, and sleep. The condominium doesn't have sentimental value to me. I'm ready to start my new life.

When I head up the ramp to my new house, I'm so tired that I almost drive off the side since the ramp doesn't have a running board. Then I hear Flo say, "A little to your right, Sweetie." But I'm having trouble steering for some reason. Somehow I manage to straighten out the chair to drive it inside the door as I enter the kitchen. After I reach the dining room table, Brian smiles and asks, "What's happening, Steven?"

I say, "Nothing." Then I feel numb, but remember I have to confirm with my lawyer that she's coming to the house tomorrow to discuss my will. I park the wheelchair next to a brown leather sofa and say, "Flo, I need to write. I need the other wheelchair, please."

"Right, Honey. James, please put Steven in his manual wheelchair. Thank you," Flo says.

"Let's go, my brother," James says, smiling at me as he moves my manual wheelchair over to my desk.

I see that my computer is up, waiting for me to write. "Thank you, James."

After he locks the brakes of the manual wheelchair, James unbuckles my seat belt and in one swoop transfers me from the electric wheelchair to the manual. Then he takes me to my desk where Flo shows him how to put the head array into the slot on the back of the chair. James turns on the computer

I take over, getting back to work. After I load CoWriter and Outlook Express, I hear Brian tell an overweight woman, "Tracey, I'm ready for bed. My butt hurts. I'm wet."

Brian backs up his electric wheelchair and heads down the hallway to his room.

I look at the clock above my computer. The time is 5:05. Tracy sighs and says, "Oh lord" before heading to his bedroom.

It's strange to me that Brian is going to bed this early. I'm just getting going with my writing.

Andy just stares at a computer screen, playing Panda Pop with the theme music blaring away. He seems to be in a trance when James yells, "Mr. Dean, move back your chair so I can take your blood sugar." Andy doesn't response. He is in another world until James slaps him hard on his shoulder and shouts, "Son, move!"

"Ouch, you're hurting me, James! Stop it! Dammit, James, you're hurting me," Andy exclaims, making the walls shake and me jump. He throws his wheelchair into reverse, allowing James to get a blood sugar reading. "What is it, James?" Andy asks.

"250," James tells him.

"I'll have six cookies, a drumstick, a candy bar and a donut," Andy shouts.

"Oh, forget it, Andy!" James exclaims.

"You son of a bitch," Andy exclaims.

"Calm down, Andy," Tracey says, appearing out of nowhere.

"I'm going to bed now," Andy screams and zooms his power chair across the living room and down and the hallway to his bedroom. "I'm ready for bed," Andy calls out in a loud voice from his room.

What have I gotten myself into, I wonder? I can't even think or read an email with all this noise. There is no email from Stasia. I remind myself that I have to be patient, but yet I feel alone. Then I remember that my people are just an email away. I feel someone tickling my arm. When I turn, I see Flo who says, "Hi, Honey. I'm sorry about Andy. Things will take time to get used to. I'm going to let Coal stay at the condo tonight. He'll be okay. The first thing in the morning I'll bring Coal here, I promise."

"Okay," I say.

"Coal will be here when you get up. I'll be back tomorrow, Honey," Flo tells me as she walks out of the front door.

I nod.

Heather comes over to me. She hugs me and says, "I'll be here for the AM shift at seven. Have a good night, Sweetie."

"Thanks," I tell her. Then I keep writing and hear the door close as Heather leaves.

I hear Andy, yelling. "You're hurting me! Put the hoyer down now, James! I said now!"

"Shut up, Mr. Dean," James exclaims.

It becomes quiet for several minutes as I write a new message. The air stinks like raw eggs gone bad. I hear Andy laughing when I write a short email to Stasia that reads:

Stasia,
I'm moved. Please keep me posted. Thank you.
Steven

After sending the email, I see Tracy carrying a full garbage bag in her hands. I hear her open the garage door. A minute later she comes back to the kitchen and sprays the large room with air fresher. In an instant the awful smell disappears. Tracey sits down at the dining room table, filling in the daily log for Brian, Andy and me. Then I see James coming out of the hallway to sit down in the leather sofa.

"Oh my God," James says, yawning and surprised I'm still up.

Tracey asks James, "Shouldn't he go to bed?"

"I don't know. Flo says that he goes to bed when he wants," James tells her.

"That won't work. He needs to go to bed! Oh, well, I'm going home, James," Tracey says, and gets up from the chair and walks out of the back door.

I have work to do. My life is about a writing career but I want to yell. I keep my mouth shut, going with the flow, listening to Amanda's words.

"Hey, Tracey, I want caramel corn," Andy yells from his bedroom.

"Oh, forget it, Andy," James shouts back.

"Okay, I want an ice-cream cone and a chocolate candy bar," Andy says, demanding in a loud voice, disrupting the whole house.

James gets up in disgust and heads back to his room. "You ask for too much and you're not getting anything else!" James exclaims as he slams Andy's bedroom door shut.

This doesn't make any sense to me. For the last month, I have been hearing that I must be an adult and treat my staff with respect, but here is Andy acting like a two-year-old. It makes me mad since I want to prove to my people that I can do this and will. It is 10:13. I decide to shut down the computer.

Karo comes out of the hallway toting a couple of empty boxes from my room. When Karo returns to the garage, I say, "I'm done, Karo. I want to go pee."

Karo removes the head array from the back of the manual wheelchair. She pushes the manual wheelchair to my bedroom. After Karo closes the bedroom door, I urinate. It takes me a couple of weeks to become accustomed to the staff assisting me with using the urinal. She empties and rinses the container out and returns it to the foot of the bed. Karo takes me back to the living room. She puts me in front of the TV and I say, "I want channel two four on TV, a pill, and root beer. Thank you."

"Let James do that for you, Steven. I'm going home, but I'll be back tomorrow," Karo tells me.

"Okay, bye," I tell her.

She waves goodbye to me before going out the door.

James changes the channel to twenty-four which is what I meant, but I said two four since it is easier for me to say. He goes to the medicine closet in the hallway to retrieve my Baclofen. Then James heads to the kitchen to fix my root beer. A couple of minutes later he brings my drink and the pill to take.

After I swallow the medication, I guzzle down the root beer in one gulp. I let out a loud burp while watching the baseball highlights on Sports Center. Then I yawn and rub my eyes with my right index finger as I think about what I have to do tomorrow. I could sleep forever but I can't.

The doorbell rings, startling me. James answers it. "Hi, Pa," James says, smiling at a young man.

"Hello. Why is he still up?" Pa asks.

"I don't know, Pa. Ask Flo. Well, good night, my brother," James says, looking at me, picking up his duffel bag, and heading out the door.

"You want to go to bed?" Pa asks me.

"No, fuck you," I yell, upon hearing that I need to go to bed. I'm an adult. My mind is full of emotions which make me feel confused and exhausted. I'm on my own, living in my own house. There is no turning back. Mom isn't coming back to rescue me. I have what I want now, but without Mom it feels hollow.

"No problem," Pa tells me and takes out his smartphone from his pants pocket. He begins to talk in rapid African speech if he uses simple broken English words like "okay" in his conversation. Pa is laughing until he hears a faint call of "Pa" from the back. "Yes, Brian. I'm coming," Pa answers, getting up to check on Brian.

Several minutes later I hear Pa empty and rinse out a urinal. It is midnight when I decide to go to bed. I wait for Pa to come. When I see him, I say, "I want to go to bed."

"You want to go to bed?" Pa asks.

"Yeah," I answer.

Pa pushes me to my room. He takes off my shoes, socks and drool-drenched shirt and says, "You need to go to bed before ten during the PM shift because I have work to do." Pa puts a white T-shirt on me that read, "Beware You Could End Up in a Novel." He picks me up without taking off my seat belt.

"Ouch," I scream.

"Oh, sorry," Pa says, pausing to take off the seat belt. He lifts me onto the bed and places a white paper sheet under me. He tugs my soiled jeans off saying, "I don't have time for this. You have to go to bed early. The PM shift does this work, not the overnight shift!" He rips off my Depends and starts to clean me up while he uses hot damp paper sheets and baby wipes. He puts my tense body on the very edge on the bed and leaves me while he gets a new Depends from my closet. Pa catches me when I'm about to fall, and when he returns to the closet for a washcloth, I begin to fall again. His phone buzzes and he answers it as I start to fall for a third time. Pa almost makes me fall out of the bed several times. He puts a new undergarment on me after he finishes cleaning me. "Do you have pajamas?" Pa asks.

"No. I want to roll over, please. I want the music on," I tell him.

Pa rolls me on my stomach. He removes the dirty paper sheet and covers me with a blanket. Then Pa turns on my clock radio before shutting off the light and closing the door.

I feel abused. I'm afraid of Pa. The pictures of Mom surround me as I listen to a classic-rock radio station. Each song makes me cry. One song in particular with the lyrics, "She is my queen; I can tell her anything," makes me think of Amanda. Then I feel I'm about to quit but I can't. I must keep my promise to Beaver River. Our dream is almost a reality. Onward, Steven! This is my life now!

I'm awake the entire night listening to music and thinking about all that has happened during the last month. When I hear the song, "This Is My Life," I sing the lyrics out aloud. It makes me remember singing those lyrics as a child and wishing I could be independent someday. Now this is finally my life! This is exciting but frightening at the same time. I don't have Mom saying, "No, you can't have it or do that." My safety net is gone. Now it's up to me to protect myself. I want to escape when the doorbell rings at seven. For a couple of minutes, I hear Heather and Pa talking about me. When the door slams, and I know that Pa has left I call, "Heather, Heather, Heather." It's strange to not be calling for Mom.

The door opens and Heather says, "Yes, Dear." She closes the door and kneels besides my bed.

"Pa says I have to go to bed before ten. I can't do that! My life is my career. That's all that I have. I'm a New York author! He forgot to take my seat belt off and I almost fell. Tracey said that I have to go to bed early, too. I just can't!"

"I'll take care of it. This is your house. We're here to take care of you! You have been through a lot. I want you to be happy here, Sweetie. Try to go back to sleep," Heather says, stroking my head until I fall asleep.

After falling into a deep sleep for fifteen or twenty minutes, I hear Brian yelling in the shower. I need to sleep, but Brian gets up early. The short sleep is better than nothing at all. Then I try to go to back sleep again, but someone is always yelling or talking on a cell phone right outside of my room. I go with the flow, following Amanda's directions and not wanting to disappoint her or Dan. Songs like "Lean on me" and "Friends Forever" are on the radio, making me bawl. Beaver River is on my mind. I say, "Beaver River, I won't give up. I promise. I need you. I'm coming."

The smell of bacon and eggs fills the air. I haven't eaten breakfast for years since it automatically comes right back up. Then I hear Andy's booming voice scream, "Hey, bitches taking away my pancakes and coconut cookies. Well, the hell with you! Get out of my room—now!"

Heather slams his bedroom door saying, "All right, Andy. Be that way. See you later when you apologize."

I'm awake now. What is going on, I wonder? It's time for me to get up. I need to write to my people. Then I shout, "Hey, hey, hey, hey."

Karo pops her head into the room, "Yes, Steven?"

"I want to get up," I tell her.

"Okay, just a minute," Karo replies.

"Okay," I say. Then I hear running water. A minute later I see Karo carrying a white bed pan of soapy water, putting it down on the garbage can.

Steven B. Salmon

I didn't take a shower since my shower chair needed to be ordered. It took five months for Medicare to approve and pay for the chair. When the chair finally arrived, the seat was too wide, making my butt fall through the hole. It was uncomfortable to sit in and it made my muscles extra tight. During my first shower, I threw up, making the mistake of eating before showering. My attendants decided that I couldn't handle taking a shower. It didn't help that some of my attendants were lazy. I didn't ask for a shower since I didn't want to hear my attendants complain about being overworked. I gave up on the idea of taking a shower, I let it die—just like having sex.

I smile when Heather enters my room with a man and a woman.

"Honey, this is Beth and Pete. They are observing Karo so we know how to take care of you. Okay?" Heather asks me.

"I understand," I say, being used to having countless caregivers see me naked. My modesty has disappeared, but I still can't pee in front of two people.

"Hi, Steven. I'm Beth," she says, grinning at me.

The man is looking at my degree on my bookshelf and says, "Stevens Point, a BS in English! I have a BA in English from Point. We're classmates!"

I'm not alone anymore. It feels good to have someone to talk to who understands being a writer. "I have a book right now in New York because of Mom and my classmates. They came when Mom died like they promised me in college. Without them I give. . ." I stop myself as I begin to cry, not noticing that I'm almost dressed.

"Let's get you up, my brother so you can get writing," Pete says as he scoops me up in his arms and puts me in my manual wheelchair.

Then Heather, Beth, and Pete leave and Karo assists me with using the urinal. Before Karo can close the door to give me privacy, Coal dashes into my room and jumps on the bed.

"Hi, Coal. How are you? I miss you. Are you okay? I love you. I'm okay. Did you eat?" I talk to Coal as he sits on the bed, watching me urinate.

Coal purrs at me before curling into a ball on the bed as he falls asleep.

Karo puts a Packers shirt on me and wraps a towel around my neck while she brushes my teeth.

After I finish spitting toothpaste into the towel, Karo takes me into the dining room to eat.

I see Brian reclining in his electric wheelchair and watching *The Price Is Right* on my own TV.

"Hey, Steven, what's happening?" Brian asks, chuckling as he lets out a big yawn. He falls asleep in his chair.

It seems strange to me that he is sleeping as my day is just starting. I'm hungry and say, "Heather, I take iced tea and fruit, please."

"Okay, you have mail. A letter from Amanda Tilley," Heather says, putting the envelope in front of me.

I start to cry knowing what it is. "Open it, please," I tell her.

Heather opens it. The card reads, "New York, New York is the place where dreams come true." She flips the card open and reads, "Your dream is coming true soon!" At the bottom of the card Amanda has written a note and it reads:

Steven,
You will do this. I have high expectations of your future.
Remember I'm just an email away. Be polite and follow
your dreams. Amanda

I break down in Heather's arms.

"Oh, Honey. What's wrong?" Heather asks me.

Pete and Beth come to listen as I say, "Amanda is my best friend from college. She and Dan live in Beaver River. They teach at Northland High school. I email them all the time and telling everything. They understand me. This is our dream! They are everything to me. I want to go to Beaver River this fall. It has been a dream of mine to go to Beaver River but I never did."

"Well, let's make it happen, my brother," Pete tells me.

Heather gets a Kleenex to wipe my tears away, saying, "It's okay. Would you still like some fruit and iced tea?"

"Yes."

Heather fixes my tea and retrieves my Baclofen from the medication closet. She gives me my pill along with my tea. Heather goes to the refrigerator to take out a fruit tray and carries it over to the table. "Do you like strawberries, blueberries, and grapes?"

"Yes," I reply.

Heather grabs a fork from the kitchen as she sits down next to me and gives me bites to eat.

I eat most of the fruit, enjoying it all when Heather says, "The guys don't eat enough fruit, but I won't have to worry about that with you."

"Yeah, I love fruit," I say, letting out a loud burp. "Candy, please. I want to read. Thank you."

"Heather, my baby," Brian says in a loud voice, spinning his power chair around and smiling at her before turning back to face the TV. He yawns and tells her, "I want bean soup and a grilled-cheese sandwich, please."

"I'll fix it," Beth says, leaning against the kitchen counter while she texts someone. She just stands there not doing anything while Heather takes off the wrapper from the peppermint before placing it in my mouth.

She pushes me to my desk to read, "What do you want to read, Sweetie?" Heather asks.

"Please go in the room and get J-u-s-t-i-c-e." I have to slowly spell out justice several times to Heather. The candy makes it hard for me to talk. Somehow I manage to get what I want.

"I'm sorry that it took me so long to understand you," Heather says, patting me on my shoulder.

I laugh, having dealt with being misunderstood all of my life. "It's no big deal."

Heather disappears into my bedroom to find the book. A minute later, Heather reappears, carrying the novel in her hands. She puts the book in front of me and opens it. Heather uses a couple of my Dad's belt buckles to keep the book open. Heather leaves me to read.

I hear the soup being dished up. "Brian, lunch is served."

"Okay, dear," Brian says, moving his wheelchair to the dining room table to eat.

It feels like Brian has just eaten breakfast. I lose myself in Larry Watson's well-written prose. It's time for me to get back to writing. Several of my writing friends have mentioned in their emails that I need to write. I want and need to write. The time to just write is hard to find. "Okay," I say, calling for someone to come turn the page.

"It'll be just a minute, dear," Heather tells me.

I will have to wait to have a page to be turned for ten or fifteen minutes sometimes.

Karo comes to turn the page.

"Thank you, Karo," I tell her.

"Eh, you're welcome, Steven."

I keep reading for a while enjoying my mentor's fine writing. A minute later I hear Brian say, "I want to go to bed, Beth. I'm wet."

"All right, let's go, Brian," Beth answers, following Brian to his room.

The time is 12:36. My day is just starting and Brian is going to bed. Andy is still in bed. I read a few more pages. Then I look out of the window and see a police car pulling into the driveway.

Andy starts screaming at the top of his lungs, "Abuse, abuse, abuse! I'm lying in my own shit!"

"Shut up, Andy," Beth yells.

Heather answers the door when the policeman rings the doorbell. She steps outside to explain to the officer what is happening with Andy. Heather takes the policeman to Andy's bedroom.

Several minutes pass before the officer emerges from Andy's room and tells Heather, "He's calmed down for now. If he's still at it again just call and we'll take care of it. Have a good day."

"Thank you, officer," Heather says.

Pete, Beth, and Heather go into his room to get Andy up.

What is going on here? I think to myself, imagining that I should be acting like a child, not Andy. The constant reminder of being on my best behavior has been impressed on me. I have to solve my own problems such as my attendants not understanding me, without getting mad. It's time for me to get working. "Karo, I want to write," I say to Karo as I spot her walking into living room.

"Okay, Steven," Karo says, coming over to put the head array in the slot on the back of the wheelchair. She turns the computer on.

"Thank you, Karo," I say, taking over the computer. Once I open my inbox, I create a new message to Beaver River. The email reads:

Beaver River,
I'm moved to my new house. It was a hard night. I cried most of the night, thinking about us. These are rough times. I have a care attendant who has an English degree from Stevens Point. He said that he would take me to Beaver River. I'm coming this fall. Steven

I send the email and create a new message to Stasia. Then I see Andy driving his electric wheelchair to his table.

"Good morning, Steven," Andy tells me before raising his voice, saying, "I want bacon and eggs for breakfast, Beth." The time is 2:33.

I laugh, hearing Beth say, "Andy, I'm leaving and it's two thirty. Bye, Steven."

"Bye," I reply, concentrating on my email to Stasia.

"All right then, I want four hot dogs with macaroni and ice cream for lunch, Heather," Andy demands.

Heather tells Andy, "It's too late for lunch! I'm going home. Take care, Steven." Heather walks out of the front door.

"Give me a candy bar then," Andy says to no one.

Tracey comes through the garage door before sitting down in a chair at the dining room table. She plays with her tablet as she looks for weird videos on Facebook like the President break dancing in the oval office. Tracey walks to Andy and asks, "Andy, what do you want for supper?"

"I want hamburger with cream of mushroom soup on four slices of bread. Cut up the bread! Oh yeah, I want cranberry juice with four ice cubes in it, please."

"All right," Tracey says. "Steven, what do you want to eat?"

"I want a hamburger, a salad, and ice cream, please." It helps that Tracey's father has Cerebral palsy and she is one of the first care attendants who worked with me at my condominium. I don't have to repeat myself or spell out words to Tracey

"Okay," Tracey tells me.

I begin writing an email to Stasia when James enters the house, walking up to me and asking, "Steven Salmon, how are you?"

"Okay," I answer, beginning to get mad with all of the interruptions when I'm working!

"Mr. Dean, my son. How are you?" James asks Andy.

"I'm good, Dad," Andy says in a booming voice and a loud laugh while the theme music of Panda Pop plays continuously in the background.

"That's good, my son," James says to Andy before walking to the dining room table.

It's quiet for now. The email to Stasia reads:

Stasia,
It was a hard night. I'm doing the best that I can, but I cried all night. Steven

I fire off the email to Stasia. Then I create a new message to write a post for Cory to publish on my blog. I start writing but am interrupted when James begins yelling at Andy, "You call yourself a man of God, but you call the cops after calling the female staff bitches! Ah Andy, I'm very disappointed in you, my son!"

"Shut up, James," Andy shouts.

"All right, if you say so," James says, walking away in disgust.

I can't write in this environment. A ding makes me jump, but I know it is Stasia. After using Escape I save the message in the drafts to write later. I use the mouse to click on the message that reads:

Dear Steven,
Hang in there. Love, Stasia

I see Karo and say, "I go pee. Thank you, Karo."

"Coming, Steven," Karo says, taking off the head array, and wheeling me to my room, assisting me to urinate. She pushes me into the dining room to eat.

James feeds me supper. He gives me my Baclofen with iced tea. After he lifts the lid to keep the food warm, James cuts up the hamburger into bites.

"No, I want vegetables," I say, looking at the mixture of carrots, snap peas, and broccoli that makes my mouth water. I'm hungry and tired!

"Okay," James says, preparing a spoonful of vegetables.

These vegetables are delicious, but James keeps mixing up my food and it drives me crazy. I notice that there is nothing on the hamburger. "Ketchup, mustard, and pickles, please," I tell him.

"What, my brother?" James asks.

"I want mustard, ketchup, and pickles," I repeat, motioning my head at the refrigerator, but luckily Tracey, who is sitting on the sofa, hears me.

Tracey gets up and takes out the condiments from the fridge. She puts a generous serving of each condiment on the burger, looking at James and saying, "You play too much!"

James wrestles with Tracey. Both of them are laughing, reminding me of Amanda and me.

I'm laughing when James puts the first bite of hamburger in my mouth, but I choke, gagging and spitting up food on my shirt.

"You need to chew your food and you have messed up your shirt," James says as he takes away my plate.

"Hey, I'm not done!" I tell him, knowing that I need to eat my meal in order to keep writing. After I take a deep breath, I eat the rest of the hamburger. Then I say, "Ice cream, please."

"You eat too much, and you want ice cream; okay," James says, dishing a bowl of chocolate ice cream.

I eat the ice cream and then I finish my tea within a few seconds. "Candy, please," I say; but James doesn't hear me since he is washing dishes and Tracey is on her tablet, laughing at something. I start to gag, but Karo sees me and puts a peppermint in my mouth.

"James, you always give Steven a candy right after he eats or he will throw up," Karo tells James in African.

"Oh, okay. I'm sorry, my brother," James says to me as Karo pushes me in front of the TV while I digest my meal.

"It's okay. I want two six on TV, please," I say to James, smiling at him.

"Yes, my brother," James tells me, switching the channel to twenty-six so I can watch the Cubs and the Brewers.

Andy is playing Panda Pop with the same theme music repeating itself nonstop. "Tracey, I have made it to the forty-eighth level on Panda Pop," Andy says but she doesn't answer him because she is heading outside to smoke.

I close my eyes and sleep for fifteen or twenty minutes. After I wake up, I say, "James, I want to write, please. Thank you."

"Yes, my brother," James says, putting me back in front of the computer.

I tap my head to bring up the inbox. Then I open the Drafts, using the mouse to get the email that I have saved for the posting. I hear Andy ask to go to bed, but I'm in my zone. Every sound and smell of this new home just disappears in my mind once I bring up CoWriter. The posting reads:

This is definitely a new life. I'm totally dependent on my staff to do their jobs. If they don't do their work, like not doing the laundry, my career will suffer. What they don't realize yet is that they are caring for a New York author! I don't need twelve or fourteen hours of sleep. My goal is to become a big-time author. I don't know if I can do this, but I have no choice now. Mom and Dad are not coming to take me home like when I was homesick at summer camp. I'm a man, handling eight care attendants, an agent, and my brand new responsibilities like remembering my debit card's pin number and my career. I will go to bed early to avoid the evil care attendant. Tomorrow is a new day.

Steven B. Salmon

Chapter Sixteen

NOT SPOILED ANYMORE

My electric wheelchair is driving down the aisles of the grocery store as I pick out food with Karo. When I see an item that I want, I say, "Karo, I want that." I use my eyes, pointing to what I want, and say, "Up, down, and over." After I see Karo grab the ice cream that I want, I say, "Yes." I choose vegetables, fruit, meat, pizza, French bread, cookies, potato chips, nachos, salsa, cheese dip, ice cream, root beer, tea, lemonade, Tide, baby wipes, and of course, cat food. If I forget to get something at the store, I will have to go without it until I go shopping again. I was spoiled having Mom run to the store whenever we wanted or needed something. I enjoy buying what I want to eat like New York strip steak. My two-hundred-and-fifty-dollars monthly food budget doesn't go very far. I use some of my spending money for the essentials such as bread and ice cream. Then I hope that I don't go over the gift certificate limit or I will have to pay for it out of my pocket—or worse, return an item.

I have doctors, wheelchairs, and communication-device appointments to go to. The days of staying home just to write are long gone. Decisions are never ending. When I ride the bus, going to these appointments, I feel proud of myself. I'm doing it. Sometimes I feel like an absolute failure. At times, I sit at the computer and cry, reading an email from a friend, like Cathy. My staff doesn't know that I'm crying amid the endless noise. Sometimes I just cry for no reason, especially in bed at night. It feels like I'm all alone, but my people are just an email away. I somehow manage to keep moving forward.

During this time, I'm writing my will for my lawyer while waiting to hear from Stasia. It's nerve racking, but my people are behind me, including Stasia. I start writing a second manuscript after Flo and Eric tell the staff that I can go to bed when I want. My new responsibilities, like communicating with Becky or my special trust beneficiary agent, have to be done during the afternoon when they are at work. At night, I write when the house is quiet until around four in the morning while the overnight care attendant sleeps on the sofa. Sometimes I have to wake up the attendant when Brian calls to go pee or when I want to go to bed, but some nights when the writing is flowing I stay up all night, greeting the AM shift before going to bed. I leave email messages to Beaver River or Stasia, saying, "Good morning. Coal kept me company through the night. It's six o'clock. I'm going to bed. Good night."

The day before Mom's funeral Stasia emails me. The message reads:

Dear Steven,
One publisher rejected the manuscript. Don't get discouraged. Eight publishers have it. Stasia

Then I forward the email to Beaver River and write.

Can I do this? Maybe someday, right? Tomorrow, we bury Mom. Steven

Dan replies first.

That's a silly question. Look at what you have achieved. You CAN make it or do anything that you want. Dan

Mac picks me up to travel to a small cemetery in southwestern Wisconsin. I'm happy to be out of my new home for the entire day, making the six-hour trek to say goodbye to Mom. It's hard to believe that this is the final goodbye. Yesterday I was working with Stasia as we try to get my book rights back from my publisher, but now I'm a son, grieving for his mother.

Mac pushes me in my manual wheelchair across the grassy knoll with my friend, Cathy at my side. My family gathers in a small circle near the edge of a soybean field. Mark, Lynn, Lexe, Courtney, Lisa, Rita, Jill, Aunt Jean, Mac, Cathy, and a couple of other cousins stand behind me.

I stare at the golden urn lying next to a tarp covering up a hole. A wreath of roses stands in front of the grave. It's a beautiful late summer day with a gentle breeze as it makes the soybeans sway. "Amazing Grace" is played. Lynn says a few words about

Mom. Then it's my turn to speak. My cousin Matt reads my poem in his baritone voice.

I break down in Aunt Jean's arms when Matt reads the poem. During the reading, a butterfly lands on the roses; and at the end of the poem, the butterfly flies away. All of us see it! Each one of us say farewell to Mom, but I'm the last to say goodbye.

Cathy pushes me up to the urn, leaving me alone there for a few minutes. Mac and Cathy are in the distance while waiting for me to wave, signaling that I'm ready to go.

I say, "Mom, thank you for everything! I have a new life. It's not easy, but I will make it. I won't give up, I promise! The book is in New York! New York, Mom! That's the dream. Goodbye, Mom."

On the way back to my new house it dawns on me that I'm in control of my life. I look at Mac, saying, "Gravel, I'm independent!"

Mac asks, "Isn't that what you wanted?"

"Yeah, but I miss Mom," Tears roll down my cheeks.

"I know," Mac tells me, patting my boney knee.

Steven B. Salmon

Chapter Seventeen

TEACHING AT BEAVER RIVER

On Monday I start working on my plans to go Beaver River. It's time to make a dream come true. I ask Heather for a calendar to pick a date to visit my best friends. The email reads:

Beaver River,
Can I come on Monday, September eighteenth? I need you! Steven

Amanda replies:

Yes, but you're teaching seven classes and I want a class outline from you.

I laugh, but I know that she is serious. Then I email Becky to rent to a van for me. In another message, I email Eric and Flo about having Pete be my attendant for the trip but not before I ask Pete if he will take me.

"Of course, let's make it a trip to remember, brother," Pete says.

It takes a lot of planning and working to organize the details for me to attend an event like the writing conference. People have to work together to make it happen. For the next three weeks, it all comes together like the slow rise of a circus tent. An outline is written and sent to Amanda, a hotel room is reserved, money is taken out of my bank account to pay for expenses, my bags are packed, and a van sits out on the driveway, waiting to take me away.

The day before I go to Beaver River Stasia emails me. The message reads:

Dear Steven,
Six publishers rejected the manuscript. Now don't get negative! You need to edit it and show the character's feelings more. Stasia

I reply.

Okay.

I sit there, crying to myself. Then I forward the email to Amanda and Dan with message that reads:

I just don't know if I can do it. I'm exhausted. I need you! Steven

I can't sleep the night before I leave.

After the Packers game, Pete and I travel up north. I just want to think to myself, but Pete keeps asking questions. "Shut up," I finally say, thinking about us.

"Not a problem, my friend," Pete tells me, driving in silence, passing forests.

I'm here in Beaver River, checking into my hotel. One dream is a reality. Tomorrow is a new day.

Monday is here. When I drive the electric wheelchair through the metal front doors, I enter the school's office and say, "I'm here to see Mrs. Tilley."

"She's expecting you. She'll be down in a minute," the secretary says, calling Amanda.

"Well, isn't that the New York author?" Dan shouts from behind the office's counter.

"No, I'm just a writer," I say.

"Steven is a New York author; right, Amanda?" Dan asks Amanda.

"Please follow me, author," Amanda tells me.

I follow her down the main hallway to the auditorium. "I'm here, Sister," I tell her when she opens the double doors. Then I follow her down the aisle to the stage.

She smiles at me and says, "It's a new life, Steven. Anything is possible now. It will happen, you know."

I begin to cry. "I know." Then I see Dan and Pete.

The three friends embrace me. "Hey, author. We need to get a microphone on you," Dan says.

"I'll be in the back. Just yell if you need me," Pete tells me, touching my arm before heading to the back of the theater.

"All that I need are my best friends," I say, smiling from ear to ear.

The three of us are working together just like in our college days, putting on the mike, doing a sound check and getting a video of Stasia ready that shows her talking about me. "The class outline is perfect, Steven. You will say a few words first, and I will repeat what you said to the students," Amanda tells me

"Okay," I say.

The bell buzzes and students start to file in, taking seats in the front row. I'm nervous and my muscles are very tight as sweat runs down my back. My mind is absorbing the moment, but it is almost too much. I relax and take a deep breath when the bell rings again. The feelings that I feel are excitement and anxiety.

"Settle down, people," Amanda tells the students, who are shuffling their feet and jabbering among each other. In an instant the class becomes quiet. "We're honored to have a future New York author here today. My friend, Steven Salmon, has Cerebral palsy which affects his speech and muscle movements. Steven uses Morse code to write since he is unable to use his hands. Steven writes ten hours a day. He's here today to talk about writing and life." Amanda says to the class. "I'm going to show a video of Steven writing. Then he'll talk and I'll interpret for him."

The video shows me tapping away and swaying my head back and forth writing with CoWriter, spelling out one letter at a time, writing a sentence, as Stasia speaks, "Steven

Salmon is a passionate author with severe Cerebral palsy, improving the lives of the disabled. His dedication is impressive. I'm proud to represent Steven as a client. He's truly a remarkable man with many talents."

The video ends. Sometimes I forget how lucky that I am to have an agent, a career, a family, and friends who love me. I see it more now that Mom is gone, but it's time to teach. For a moment, I look at the students before saying, "Hi, I'm Steven Salmon. I have Cerebral palsy. That's why it's hard to understand me. Thank you for inviting me to your school. It's been a dream of mine to come here. Today, I'll talk about writing and life."

"Life is like writing. It goes up and down. An author's life is filled with disappointments, rejections, deadlines, and heartache," I take a pause, starting to cry.

Amanda says to the class, "Please excuse us for a couple of minutes."

Dan follows Pete down to the front row. After the three friends embrace me and Amanda wipes my tears with a Kleenex, she says, "It'll happen, you know. It's going to take more work and time."

"That's nothing new to our author, right?" Dan asks me.

"I know," I say, looking at Amanda and Dan.

Amanda and Dan stand next to me for a few minutes. She tells me, "Hey, you're here to teach my students that by working hard and following their dreams the American dream can happen."

"I hear you, Sister," I say, gathering myself before teaching the rest of the day while shredding more tears and laughing with my two best friends.

The message that I received from Amanda and Dan as I taught was that I could accomplish anything now, including becoming a New York author. I thought about what I had to do to visit Beaver River, making the once impossible dream come true. Plus, I did it without Mom or my cousin, Mac, including urinating in different places with Pete assisting me.

I had the strength to battle onward, overcoming problems and making decisions like buying a manual wheelchair while writing another book as I worked with Stasia on the first book. Days overlap each other now. I sleep when I don't have any energy to write, believing that someday I will be published by a big-time publisher. At times, it seems impossible, but that is a life of a writer!

**Visit Steven B. Salmon at
www.stevenbsalmon.com.**

Made in the USA
Columbia, SC
12 June 2020